Half-Dolls
PriceGuide

by
Sally Van Luven and Susan Graham

Published by
Hobby House Press, Inc.
Grantsville, Maryland
www.hobbyhouse.com

Dedication

THIS BOOK is dedicated to
My wonderful family members for their encouragement and love
and
My very special friends — Norma Smith and Gaby Grollmuss.

THE DOLL PRICES given within this book are intended as value guide
rather than arbitrarily set prices. They are recorded as accurately as possible,
but in the case of errors, typographical, clerical or otherwise the author and publisher
assume neither liability nor responsibility for any loss incurred by users of this book.

Additional copies of this book may be purchased at $22.95
(plus postage and handling) from:

Hobby House Press, Inc.
1 Corporate Drive, Grantsville, MD 21536
1-800-554-1447
WWW.HOBBYHOUSE.COM
or from your favorite bookstore or dealer.

Printed in the United States of America

ISBN: 0-87588-670-1

Edited by Virginia Ann Heyerdahl | Designed by David Williams

Acknowledgments

THIS BOOK would have been impossible to write if it were not for the people who provided knowledge, photographs and encouragement when I most needed their special support. I would like to express my gratitude to all who have shown their interest in this endeavor.

My family who ignored my messy house, lousy meals and despair, but picked up the pieces and encouraged me to continue. ~ Susan Graham who read and reread the script and added the pertinent details so necessary in increasing the readers' understanding. ~ Gabrielle Grollmuss, who has been so generous with her time and vast knowledge of half-dolls, and her husband, Gert Grollmuss, for his efforts and photography. ~ Dave and Deryn Gipp who generously shared photographs of their museum-quality collection. I appreciate the communications I have received from them and am awed by their vast knowledge. ~ Norma Smith who provided a listening ear as well as many photographs from her collection and helped me find half-dolls to fill in missing pieces. ~ Janet and Brian Day for their excellent photographs, knowledge and faith in my ability to provide helpful information about value at a time when support was most important. ~ Shona and Marc Lorrin who graciously answered my e-mails and shared information that might help me. ~ Roland Schlegel and Susan Bickert who continue to produce items from the antique molds which might have been lost forever had they not decided to continue production and for the sale of old catalogs to increase my own knowledge. ~ Jereune Theber for the photographs she sent. ~ Rick Saxman, Greg Mountcastle and Richard Wright for patiently answering my questions and allowing me to photograph the half-dolls they have for sale as well as giving me the value of each. ~ Jan Lewis and Susan Girardot for providing pricing information. ~ Biri Fay for selling me important Hertwig & Co. articles. ~ The dealers of NADDA for their support, especially Sheila Needle and Geri Gentile. ~ Shirley Bertrand for steering me to information I might have overlooked. ~ Kathy Adams and Joyce Stock for sending me the David Cobb antique catalogs and the prices realized. ~ Dolores Smith and Arlene Ricter of Richard Withington's Auction staff for allowing me to photograph their items prior to sale and for assisting me. ~ Sherry White and Kathy Trenter of Hobby House Press, Inc., and especially to Virginia Ann Heyerdahl for her editorial expertise.

Table of Contents

from
Galluba & Hofmann:
Hairdos
Without Hats
page 25

Part Two: Models with a Specific Feature ~ 84

from
**Dresser Figurals:
Powder Jars
page 97**

Preface

In the early part of the twentieth century, clothing was designed and completed within the home. Young women were expected to learn basic stitching, and beyond this, to develop an interest in dressmaking. Flour sacks made of fabric were purchased with design in mind. A manufacturer of dress patterns, *The Delineator*, provided the dress patterns. Objects—half-dolls—that might induce interest were made to entice a young lady to sew.

These half-dolls illustrated the varied fashions from the time of Egyptian rule to the beginning of the 1940s and World War II. This period covers the fashions of the medieval ages, colonial years, French Revolution, the Biedermeier styles of lace, satins and floral patterns, and the angular art deco period with the independence of the flapper era. Each half-doll was molded so that the hairstyle was designed to match the appropriate style of the bodice. The pincushion, tea cozy, lamp or other type "skirt" covering would be designed to complete the fashion statement represented by the model.

Porcelain manufacturers designed a few half-dolls that represented the headdress of early rulers such as Caesar and Cleopatra. Because there are few models available, examples are ardently sought. Perhaps because costuming required knowledge of the entire costume of the period, they are found without a dressmaker's additional embellishment.

During the Medieval or Renaissance period (1350 to 1520) clothing had a high empire waist. Elaborate headdresses were covered with gauze and lace placed over metals embellished with jewels. Several models by Dressel, Kister & Co. illustrate the dress. Galluba & Hofmann also produced two known figurines representing this period.

In the Colonial period (from approximately 1770 through 1810) the hat was made as a bonnet. At times, the cap fit snuggly against the head with a brim that would protect the lady from receiving too much sun that might color her face. Sleeves were puffed slightly below the shoulder. The hair was swept into an updo, although ringlets were common as well. Shawls were placed over the shoulders. The camisole and bloomers were underclothing. Half-dolls, molded in camisoles, were designed by several porcelain manufacturers.

During the French Revolution, in the years 1790 through 1815, portraits of Marie Antoinette show extravagant headwear and clothing. Clothing was designed as a sexual enticement. Bouffant style hair was powdered and dressed with beads, flowers and feathers. Hats were trimmed with colorful ostrich feathers, more flowers, jewels and ribbons. The waistline was tiny, ending in the shape of a "V." Shawl collars, sometimes tied at the front, accented the bodice. The sleeves on the bodice fit close to the arm.

The Victorian era lasted from 1837 through 1901. The Victorian woman had an hourglass figure with a small waist and wore skirts that were made full and held away from the body through the use of underskirts and bustles of crinoline or boning. The bodice of the dress showed cleavage, as the shoulders and the upper part of the breasts were bare. The dress often had a shawl. The sleeves were full with ruffles and puffs. Finally, a lady's hair was worn in ringlets.

During the Biedermeier period, dress became very colorful. Floral patterns were embroidered on the bodice of the dress. Half-dolls represented the style of the middle class woman who began to wear elegant clothing. The shawl remained casually draped about the shoulders.

The public eventually became bored with the extravagances of fashion; thus came the angular art deco period around 1918, lasting into the early 1930s. A woman of fashion wore clothing reflecting this trend. Stripes were woven or printed on fabric that was made of linen, cotton and silk. The severe hairdo appeared and facial makeup was evidenced by lips brightly painted and eye makeup that might remind an observer of a raccoon. The period of art deco heralded the coming of the flapper. The flapper's hair was short, cut just under the ear lobe. The chest was flattened in a boyish fashion. The bodice was a low-cut blouse ending at the hip line. The waist disappeared. Skirts fit close to the body and fabric was cut on the bias. The hat was a felt cloche.

The half-doll determines the appropriate skirt for the pincushion. However, the manufacturers were not satisfied with providing half-dolls to be used as pincushions only. With the introduction of the half-doll came other uses such as a top of a broom, hat holders, puff holders and then as part of a lamp. Drip catchers were then introduced. These were diminutive figures that sat atop a teapot to catch drips. Eventually the manufacturers created even more objects such as the powder patter, the perfume bottle, the powder container and others.

With the onset of World War II, the production of the half-doll ceased. The workers were needed in the war effort and half dolls were considered trivial. The factories were vacated or were made to produce war articles. The fragile half-dolls were easily broken, viewed as "clutter" and tossed away. The objects were perceived as of little value which could be purchased for pennies. Because so many were made in Germany, American households eliminated a number of items associated with that country. So, even though thousands of these half-dolls were produced, some of the figurines are very rare.

These "nippes," as half-dolls are called, are gaining popularity. The interest is international and contagious. It is important that collectors have a value guide to provide information providing replacement cost values. This book is not based upon inconsistent Internet values but, instead, the values suggested are those that would determine the replacement cost for items that are lost, stolen or broken.

The values listed are retail prices paid for a half-doll if purchased from an antique store, doll show or dealer. The values reflect dolls in mint condition. To be considered mint, the costuming may show slight wear and appear clean. The half-doll should retain full paint and not be chipped or cracked. The facial features should be carefully molded and "crisp" and skillfully painted. Half-dolls that are poorly produced have lesser value and some of these are illustrated.

This book is intended as a guide only. Prices fluctuate from area to area, country to country and at different times. Most dealers welcome questions and will provide information if asked. If a price seems unreasonable, question why or what has determined its value. Lastly, buy only the half-dolls you can love and appreciate.

Introduction

Perhaps you marveled at your grandmother's pincushion doll, which she allowed you to touch or even hold. It was so pretty with the little bisque half-doll at the top and the beautiful overskirt that made the pincushion. Maybe you were in an antique store and saw a few delicate half-dolls with features so exact, you knew you had a dozen places where they might be displayed. Or you received a little powder box as a gift. Now you have several of these little dolls and would like to know their value.

In searching for these endearing half-dolls, I discovered the need for an affordable compact book that could serve as a guide. This book was written with the hope it will be helpful to the half-doll collector. Included are half-dolls from the easily found and inexpensive to those of museum quality, with over three hundred illustrations for possible identification.

While half-dolls were made of wax, wood and cloth as well as bisque and china, this book will cover only the bisque and china half-dolls, and related half-doll items, produced by the half-doll manufacturers from similar molds.

The items listed here are frequently considered a part of half-doll collections. Each area will be presented with historical information, any labels and marks along with mold numbers and physical descriptions.

Although half-dolls were initially referred to as pincushion dolls, that description is too confining, as the half-doll became so many more items. It was made as an object for teens and adults but was most often sold as an incomplete figure, lacking thighs, legs and feet. At the waist, the half-doll's base was

generally wider than the waist and had several holes made to join the figure to something else such as the objects listed here.

1.

Pincushion: The most commonly found use of half-dolls is that of a pincushion. The upper portion of the pincushion was a bisque or china half-doll while the bottom-half (beneath a pretty overskirt) was a cloth body filled with sawdust, cork bits, straw or cotton, and bowl-shaped with a solid bottom. It was the bottom portion that was used as a pincushion.

2.

Brooms: Little brooms were used to dust lint from dresses and suits or crumbs from a table after dinner. The top portion of the broom would be the half-doll with straw coming out of the lower section of the doll. To hide the area where the doll is joined to the straw, the broom is wrapped with a ribbon. These brooms were half-dolls of people or animals. One little broom was actually used to apply suds to the face when shaving.

3.

Powder puff dolls: Half-dolls were sewn on a wire frame, which held the doll about 5in (13cm) high. Over the wire would be a cotton underskirt with an organdy skirt over all. The organdy overskirt had pockets at the hem of the skirt which held little velour powder puffs.

4.

Powder puffs: Half-dolls were often sewn or glued on the powder puff to be used as a handle for the puff.

5.

Patter puffs: Bas-relief figural bisque or china heads were placed upon a powder puff that had a wooden handle approximately 12in (31cm) long.

6.

Drip catchers: Tiny figures sat atop a teapot with a little sponge under the spout to catch the drips. These are generally birds and butterflies, but there are small figurines of people as well.

7.

Powder boxes: Boxes that held powder were generally made as a figurine cut in two with the upper portion becoming the lid. Round or oval, these were shaped to fit the powder puff that would be placed into the box in order to receive the powder. Another powder box was a two-part figurine composed of a powder dish that stood on legs or a base with the figurine on a powder puff. When the two pieces were placed together it made a completed figurine. The top of the first doll was generally a flapper or Pierrette (a female clown). The lower half of her torso was a powder puff surrounded by swan's-down. Below was a Pierrot (the male clown) holding the legs of the Pierrette.

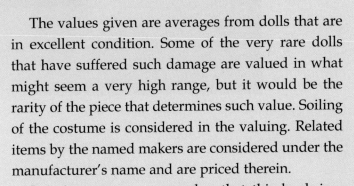

8.

Trinket Boxes: Little boxes of china or bisque that held hairpins, hatpins, hair and other items that might be considered necessary to grooming. The bottom of the box could be any shape and the lid had a figure—often a child, a bathing beauty, flapper or Victorian lady.

9.

Egg timers: Egg timers had enough "sand" in which to time a minute. The figurine was made of china with an area of brass attached to the glass, which held the sand. The brass portion contained a spring or rivet that could be turned so that the sand could flow downward.

10.

Hat holders: Very rare items composed of a doll holding a stick, which was padded at the top to hold a hat.

11.

Perfume bottles: Little china or bisque figurines which might have held a cork and glass rod, or just a little lid that was incorporated into the total figurine. The bottle contained perfume or smelling salts.

12.

Lamps: Figures of porcelain or composition were used for illumination. The top of the lamp might be the area with the light, although the lamp may have had the light under the skirt that served as the shade.

13.

Bathing beauties: Half-dolls were frequently molded as nudes. However, companies made full-bodied nude figurines as well. Some of these became the top half of a powder puff or other object. The bottom of the figurine had the four holes with which to sew the doll onto the object. There were full figurines designed to be placed on an object without being sewn or glued on. They could be dressed with a bathing suit or nude. Some of the finest nude figurines were dressed in net suits.

The values given are averages from dolls that are in excellent condition. Some of the very rare dolls that have suffered such damage are valued in what might seem a very high range, but it would be the rarity of the piece that determines such value. Soiling of the costume is considered in the valuing. Related items by the named makers are considered under the manufacturer's name and are priced therein.

It is important to remember that this book is a value **guide**, and, as such, is intended to help you determine a realistic value for your doll. It is important to remember that in the United States, prices in various regions may differ greatly for the same doll. Dolls in the Midwest tend to be the lowest in price, while the same doll in the East or in California might be much higher.

Finally, the information regarding valuing is a retail value determined at the time of a sale and was averaged from data gathered from auctions, antique malls, doll shows and the Internet. Because there has not been an overall guide since 1975, in many instances, I have had to use averages that might represent a large range, my own judgment or the knowledge of a collector with years of experience. Many very gracious collectors have given freely of their time and knowledge in the preparation of this material.

PART ONE

Manufacturers

A.W. Fr. Kister

In 1835, a Blankenhain porcelain factory bookkeeper named Louis Oels asked Prince Friedrich Gunther von Schwarzburg for permission to produce porcelain in Scheibe-Alsbach. The Prince did not grant permission to the Scheibe factory until 1840. In the meantime, Oels had sold his factory (which painted porcelain made by other factories) to Friedemann Greiner and Daniel Kämpfe in 1839. In 1844, Johann Friedrich Andreas Kister and a Mr. Dressel purchased the porcelain factory. From 1863 into the 1890s, Johann's son, August Wilhelm Friedrich Kister, was the sole owner of the factory.

The village of Scheibe was perfect for the manufacture of porcelain. The ample supply of wood from the Thuringian forests was used to fuel the factory. Kaolin and sand from the area were used in the porcelain mixture. People living in Scheibe and the neighboring villages provided the labor to produce porcelain.

The factory finally closed in 1996.

The numbers marking some of the half dolls are five-digit numbers beginning with "11---." The bases on the dolls may be narrow or wide. Aside from the half-dolls presented here, there are others manufactured by A.W. Fr. Kister on page 94 (lower left illustration), page 116 (bottom illustration) and page 127 (bottom illustration).

Ladies

This model wears a beautiful hat much like the one in the portrait of Madame Molé-Raymond that was painted by Marie Louise Elisabeth Vigée-Lebrun.

- 3½in (9cm) $395
- 4¼in (11cm) $450
- 5½in (14cm) $550

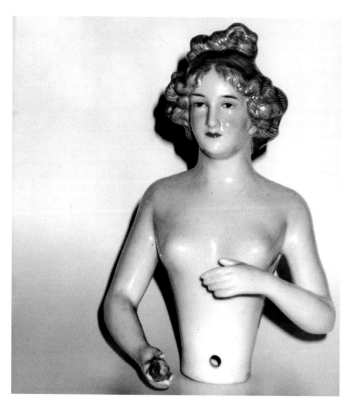

This young woman wears a band in her curly hair. Her curls are placed toward the top and back of her head and she holds a rose.

- 5in (13cm) $1150

Dressel, Kister & Co.

The Dressel, Kister & Co. porcelain factory began making porcelain in Passau, Bavaria, in 1853. The factory remained in business for approximately one hundred years. From the beginning, this Bavarian factory produced figurines in large numbers. One of the reasons these figurines were so successful was the skill in modeling and painting by the artisans who made them.

Sculpting themes centered on subjects from famous paintings and well-known personalities. The factory also designed a group of half-dolls dressed in fashions from the medieval era. One of the primary means of identifying Dressel, Kister & Co. half-dolls is the narrow base. The mark for the company resembles a "G" with a long tail heading downward. The outside of the "G" has rays. (See Appendix A, page 131.)

Medieval Figures

THE medieval figurines range in size from 2½in (6cm) to 11½in (29cm) high. These figurines and half-dolls are of exceptional quality and beauty and coveted by collectors. As a result, they bring very high prices.

The models were sculpted wearing full gowns trimmed with molded ermine fur and beaded decorations representing jewels and gold. The headdress was an ornate appendage sitting gracefully upon the head. In their hands, they hold jewels, books, birds, boxes or other items of beauty.

OPPOSITE PAGE: In order to illustrate the beauty of the medieval figurines, full-size models, rather than half-dolls, are shown.

- 7½in (19cm)   No. 4469 $1800
- 9½in (24cm)   No. 4567 $2350
- 11½in (29cm)   Nos. 4658, 4659 $2500

This model has a pointed hat and holds a book. Although her finger is broken, she remains an expensive half-doll. She was molded with either stationary arms or with arms attached with elastic string.

 - 4¾in (12cm) $2300

This half-doll holds a bird and is based on a painting entitled *Eude des Ursins*.

 - 4¾in (12cm) $2400

Victorian Women

A very popular series by Dressel, Kister & Co. features half-dolls with flowers in their hair, painted in such detail that individual strands are represented through the brush strokes. Each figure holds one rose, all of which are applied individually, and the wreath differs from half-doll to half-doll. The arms are away from the body and were molded in varied positions.

RIGHT: This example has a wreath in her hair and is holding a rose.

▪ 1½in (4cm)	$225
▪ 3¾in (9cm)	$275
▪ 4¾in (12cm)	$395

LEFT: This model was molded with much less detail than generally found on Dressel, Kister & Co. figurines. She lacks the narrow waist of the half-dolls of this company and might not be recognized as a Dressel, Kister & Co. figurine, although marked with the symbol. She is found holding a rose or with the rose absent and was manufactured in many sizes.

- 3¼in (8cm) $150
- 4in (10cm) $165

Like many other companies a model was made with arms outstretched in the manner of the painting of Mademoiselle Marie Anne de Cupis de Camargo by Nicolas Lancret entitled *La Camargo Dancing*.

- 3½in (9cm) $650
- 3¾in (9cm)   No. 4920 $675

This figure holds a rose, with a rose on each side of her hair (rather than the wreath).

- 3¼in (8cm)   No. 4275 $325
- 4¾in (12cm)   No. 4274 $450
- 5⅞in (15cm) $600

Values for a model holding grapes with a wreath of leaves in her hair are close to the values for the model shown above.

This model is very unusual. The same face is on the front and back of the figure. Her curls are well defined by modeling and fine brush strokes. Her gown was painted in colors of light green, pink or blue. She was designed to be used as a handle and was made in several sizes.

- 2½in (6cm) $185
- 3¾in (9cm) $305
- 4¾in (12cm) $450

Ladies With Hats

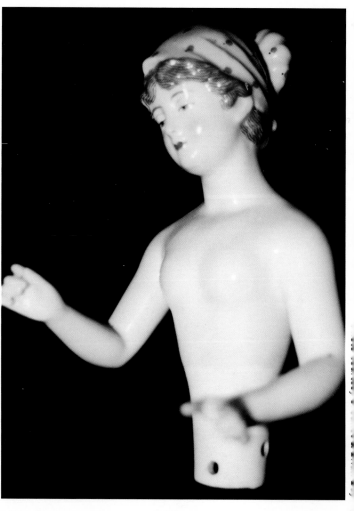

This figure wears a scarf knotted in the back with hair molded in short curls. This model was made with stationary or jointed arms. She is very difficult to find and treasured among Dressel, Kister & Co. collectors.

- 4½in (12cm) $2200
- 5¼in (13cm) $3000

Under the wide brim hat, this model with long flowing hair was molded after a portrait of Madame Molé-Raymond painted by Marie Louise Elisabeth Vigée-Lebrun.

- 4in (10cm)   No. 3993 $675
- 5½in (14cm)   No. 3992 $908

This example is a lady wearing a large hat tilted at a rakish angle. Her hat is found in pastel colors of pink, lavender, green or blue. In her hand is a single rose. Her arm, molded away from her body, can vary in positions.

- 2½in (6cm) $235
- 3¾in (9cm) $325
- 5¼in (13cm)   No. 3986 $585

This model with the colonial mobcap was molded both as a nude and dressed in a colonial style. Further, her arms were either stationary or joined to the torso with elastic so they could be positioned.

- 3½in (9cm) $485
- 4½in (12cm)   No. 4916 $750

Children

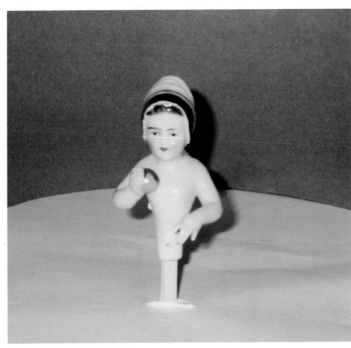

This child wears a close-fitting cap outlined in gold and holds an apple in his right hand.

- 3¼in (8cm)   No. 4136 $400

This child wears a pastel beret.

- 3½in (9cm)   No. 4133 $325

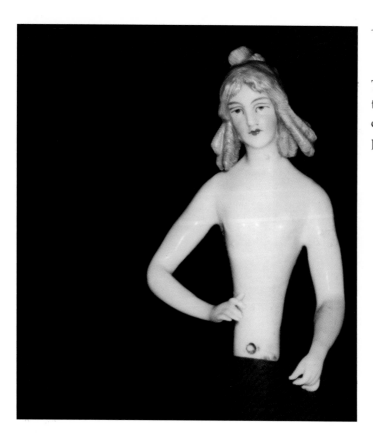

Young Woman

This young woman has several ringlets falling toward the front of her face, while her hair is molded in upward curls at the back of her head. Her hair is blonde, or painted as a powdered wig.

- 4¾in (12cm) $600

Pierrots and Pierrettes

This is a mold of a Pierrette, found in six graduated sizes from 1¾in (5cm) to 6in (15cm). Her hands are clasped together, her head is tilted to the side and she wears a black skullcap with three curls showing.

- 1¾in (5cm) $150
- 2½in (6cm) $275
- 3¾in (9cm) $395
- 4¼in (11cm) $485
- 5¼in (13cm) $635
- 6in (15cm) $785

Foulds & Freure

Robert Foulds, Sr., founded the New York Foulds & Freure importing company in 1842 and was succeeded by his son, Robert Foulds, Jr., as owner of the company. Foulds & Freure did not manufacture the half-dolls they imported.

Around 1891, Maurice Alexander, the father of Beatrice Alexander (the future founder of the Alexander Doll Company), befriended the owners of the firm. Maurice was interested in antique dolls and toys and the Foulds & Freure Company was known as wholesalers and importers of toys, dolls and novelties.

The company sold half-dolls as late as 1940. The Aelteste Volkstedt porcelain factory was one of the German porcelain factories that made half-dolls for this company. A few half-dolls were marked with the name "Foulds & Freure" as well as the mark of a porcelain factory and were produced according to the high standards of the Foulds & Freure Company. For the purpose of identification, the dolls sold by this company are those that are identified and illustrated in this section.

The mold numbers known are 630, 761, 766, 769, 828, 9001, 9002, 9003, 9475, 9476, 9477, 9613, 9615, 9618, 9619, 9620, 9622, 9623, 9624 and 9667 as well as legs numbered 9755 and a base numbered 9757.

Arms Separate from Body

LEFT & RIGHT: The very art deco model shown in these illustrations has a beautifully molded slender and elongated body, characteristic of the 1920s. She has been painted with two variations in her hairstyle — one is with silver and the other with gold streaks representing, perhaps, a hair net. Her hands are gracefully poised, but the fingers are not defined. Her eyes have a slanted and sensual appearance and are well defined. Her mouth is painted in a heart shape with a slight white space between the lips.

- 4½in (12cm)
  (unknown mark)
  $385

LEFT: This half-doll has been found in three sizes. She is an art deco model and wears her hair in a short wavy "bob." It is painted either gold or silver and she wears a necklace that matches the hair color. Her arms reach gracefully upward with the right hand raised toward her chin and the other held outward.

▪ 3in (8cm)	No. 9003	$285
▪ 3½in (9cm)	No. 9002	$325
▪ 4in (10cm)	No. 9001	$385

ABOVE: This example may not belong to this grouping, but is included because her mouth, arms and hands are similar to the previously described models. She wears an elongated dress with a high collar.

▪ 3½in (9cm)	$175
▪ 4½in (12cm)	$185

LEFT: This is a model of Mrs. Sarah Siddons.

▪ 4½in (12cm)	No. 9618	$390
▪ 5½in (14cm)	No. 9619	$485

Photo courtesy of Dave & Deryn Gipp

The company of G. H. Macheleid, a founder of the Volkstedt-Rudolstadt porcelain factory, produced this half-doll. She wears her hair in a Victorian style and her bodice reflects the same era.

- 5½in (14cm) $450

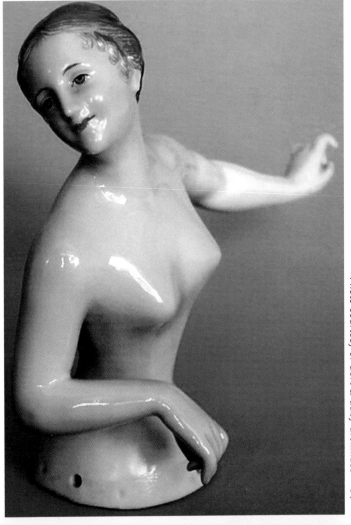

This half-doll, unlike the ones previously described, has hair pulled to the back of her head in a dancer's chignon. Her left arm is outstretched with her fingers beautifully defined while her right arm is bent with her hands at the level of her base. She has the early Volkstedt-Rudolstadt mark inside her base.

- 5in (13cm)   No. 9624 $480

Hands Touching Body

LEFT: This art deco woman, wearing a green, black and red turban and an elongated bodice, has her hands under her chin. Her eyes are outlined and she has the heart-shaped mouth with the white line between the lips.

3⅞in (10cm)	No. 555-*	$275
4½in (12cm)	No. 5400	$365
4⅝in (12cm)	No. 5496	$390
5¼in (13cm)	No. 5255	$500

Missing number illegible.

ABOVE: This art deco half-doll is very similar to the one shown in the illustration **TOP LEFT**. Both have hands clasped, both wear the same earrings, both have a turban — however, this model's turban is black with a red band. Both turbans have a wide decoration at the back of the head. This model's hands are at the breast level and she wears a blue dress.

4¾in (12cm)	No. 5485	$365

This half-doll has both arms against her body. She has a band around her head and her hair is cut in a "bob." She wears a yellow blouse and has three bracelets on her right arm. Her eyes are poorly defined.

- 4½in (12cm)
  No. 9615
  $275

Photo courtesy of Norma Smith

Galluba & Hofmann

Hugh Galluba and Georg Hofmann founded the Galluba & Hofmann porcelain factory in Ilmenau in 1891 (it closed in 1937). Galluba & Hofmann made a variety of porcelain products, including figurines, bathing beauties and small knickknacks known as "Nippes."

The history and products of the Galluba & Hofmann porcelain factory remained a mystery until Hobby House Press, Inc., published the English version of the Ciesliks' *German Doll Encyclopedia* in 1985. Marc and Shona Lorrin also described the history and products of this Ilmenau factory in their 1999 self-published book *The Half-Doll with Related Makers and Values, Volume I.*

The Galluba & Hofmann factory remained an active producer of porcelain figurines until around 1938. The factory closed prior to the end of World War II. Yet, the fine workmanship of the figures contributes to their present-day exceptional value. Today, collectors consider a half-doll manufactured by this company an important asset to their collections. The figurines represent workmanship that

excels when compared to other examples from the turn of the century. The figurines are beautifully sculpted and finely painted.

It is very difficult to find a sufficient number of half-dolls to provide the reader with pertinent information or an accurate value. Rather, the values given are based upon a small sampling. The figurines do not have the company's mark. Therefore, identification is accomplished through examination of features such as an elongated neck, glazing on the inside of the base and a base that is wide when compared to other half-dolls (with the exception of those by F. & W. Goebel). The base is enclosed from the waistline upward with only a small hole that would allow heat to escape. Most of the numbers imprinted on the base are four numbers such as 5738. The numbers can be on the outside or inside of the base.

The bonnets on the ladies are elaborate, as is the clothing. The upper eyelids are accented with a red line, the hands are well defined and the arms on the models are slender. Above the base is a narrow waistline creating an hourglass figure when dressed.

Nudes

This figurine represents superb workmanship. It is that of a young woman with her hair in ringlets and, in her hand she holds a cameo. She was made either nude or clothed with a shawl about her shoulders and draped around her arm.

NUDE:
- 4¼in (11cm)   No. 9806 $500

DRESSED:
- 5¼in (13cm)   No. 9828 $650

Wigged Ladies

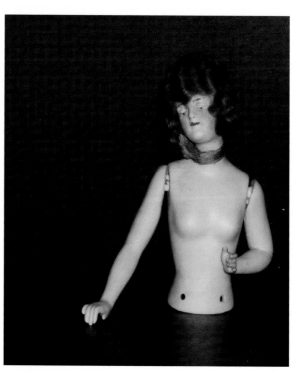

This lady carries a basket of flowers. Her dress, with short and full sleeves, is draped off her shoulders. Her original wig is parted in the center and beautifully made. She was molded wearing a very large hat, as well as a wigged model.

WIGGED:
- 5½in (14cm)   No. 5645f $800

WITH A HAT:
- 5½in (14cm)   No. 5645 $800

This model is made of unglazed porcelain (bisque that has a flesh-colored matte finish) She has arms separate from the body and attached with elastic cord. She is nude and has a slender elongated neck with her head tilting to the side. Her hairdo represents the style of the 1920s. Her arm extends beyond her waist. This model does not have the solid base as found in most Galluba & Hofmann half-dolls.

- 5½in (14cm)   No. 3806 $425

LEFT: This half-doll is bisque. Her arms are strung with elastic cord which has stretched with age, allowing the arms to slightly drop from the shoulders. This can be corrected by restringing with new elastic cord. She wears her hair in a Victorian style with long ringlets falling over her shoulder and retains her original cap. She was manufactured with fine detail.

- 4¼in (11cm)   No. 3659 $625

The same model as shown on the **LEFT** was made with arms permanently attached, like the majority of half-dolls. Her facial features are the same and her head is tilted, but she has a different wig. The only difference (besides the arm attachment) is the rose held in the right hand. It is possible that at least two more models of this half-doll exist — one with an elastic-attached arm holding a rose in her hand.

- 3½in (9cm)   No. 5692 $425

Hairdos Without Hats

Photo courtesy of Norma Smith

This lovely model, with her head turned to the side, has a wreath of flowers in her hair and holds a gold compact in her hand. She represents Marie Thérèse Louise de Savoie-Carignan, Princess de Lamballe, a friend of Marie Antoinette.

- 4in (10cm)　　No. 5706　　　$750

This young lady, with her powdered Victorian hairdo, holds a music book in her hands. This half-doll is artistically designed, sculpted and painted. She is very rare and highly desired.

- 2¾in (7cm)　　No. 8479　　　$565
- 6in (15cm)　　No. 9250　　　$1250

This young woman, with blonde hair in ringlets, is playing a musical instrument. She appears to be enjoying her music. Like each of the Galluba & Hofmann half-dolls, she is exquisitely sculpted and painted.

- 4½in (12cm)　　No. 5642　　$455

Hats

THE hats molded by the Galluba & Hofmann artists are beautifully sculpted. They have beads, feathers, bows and very wide brims. They are called high-crowned Leghorns but, when elaborately trimmed with feathers, flowers and bows, they are called Gainsborough hats, inspired by the paintings by Thomas Gainsborough of ladies from around 1775. *The Morning Walk*, a painting in the National Gallery of London, illustrates such an example.

In this example, the lady wears a Gainsborough hat with a large brim that is tilted rakishly to the side. The top of the hat is decorated with flowers. Her bodice is laced at the front with a white shawl collar and full sleeves. In each hand she holds a rose.

- 5in (13cm) $725

This lady wears her Gainsborough hat with the crown tilted upward on both sides. The feathers are toward the back of the hat and the bow is at the front. Her shawl is worn over her shoulders with a pink blouse underneath. The sleeves to her blouse fit against her slender arms and she holds a letter in her hands.

- 4¾in (12cm) $600

This model holds a watering can. Her hat, however, has the same large upturned brim as the lady in the illustration on the LEFT, but it has a ribbon at the front and large feathers at the top. Her bodice has a high collar with the front of her bodice designed as a square inset trimmed in gold and a ruffle around the inset. A ribbon on the front of the dress matches the ribbon on the hat.

- 3¼in (8cm) $750

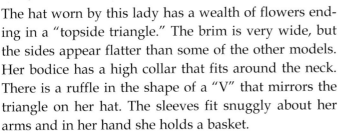

The hat worn by this lady has a wealth of flowers ending in a "topside triangle." The brim is very wide, but the sides appear flatter than some of the other models. Her bodice has a high collar that fits around the neck. There is a ruffle in the shape of a "V" that mirrors the triangle on her hat. The sleeves fit snuggly about her arms and in her hand she holds a basket.

- 5in (13cm)   No. 4927 $750

The hat on this half-doll is another elaborate confection of flowers and feathers. The brim is tilted on both sides. The blouse fits the body snuggly, as do the sleeves. On the top of the blouse is a double row of ruffles. Her waist is very slender in the manner of the Galluba & Hofmann half-dolls.

- 5in (13cm) $750

Children

LEFT: This child holds a daisy. Her beautiful Dutch cap is lavishly decorated with tiny molded beads and she wears a simple bodice with a striped shawl. Her little face has the chubby roundness of a young child.

- 4¼in (11cm) $350

RIGHT: The child shown on the left was made as a delft model, seen in the illustration on the right, a style with an underglaze in colors of blue.

- 4½in (12cm) $285

F. & W. Goebel

The F. & W. Goebel porcelain factory began as a family business around 1778 producing marbles, slates and slate pencils. In 1871, brothers Franz and William* asked the ruling Duke to allow them to produce porcelain. The Duke denied permission until 1876 when the Goebels were finally allowed to build their first porcelain factory. The name of the factory was changed to W. Goebel Porzellanfabrik in 1893 when William became president. It is still in business in Germany today and is best known as the manufacturer of the Hummel figurines. However, it is not the Hummels that will be covered here, but rather the beautiful half-dolls that were produced from around the end of World War I until the late 1930s.

Some of the figurines still carry the gold rectangular label with the Goebel trademark — a bee-shaped crown atop an intertwined "W" and "G." The figurines are beautifully molded, finely painted and desired by collectors. The bases of these half-dolls are generally wide although not always so. While F. & W. Goebel as well as other porcelain manufacturers, made half-dolls that were molded with items suggesting the serving of chocolate, the "chocolate dolls" are presented in another section. The half-dolls featured here are modeled after famous personalities and period women such as the Victorian, the colonial and the flapper as well as children. The Biedermeier series are designated by flower decals while other models do not have floral decoration.

*In German, "William" is "Wilhelm" and it appears both ways in references. Here "William" will be used.

Famous Personalities

THE F. & W. Goebel artists sculpted half-dolls of several ladies of the royal court and the famous artisans who would have entertained them.

NEAR & FAR RIGHT: Fanny Elssler, an Austrian ballerina, is seen in these two photos. Her hair is molded as a bun atop the back of her head. She wears a molded strand of beads and roses in her hair with short ringlets about her face. Her arms are molded in different positions, although not touching her body. Her head can face downward or straight ahead. She was sculpted as a nude in several different sizes and is a very popular model.

Photo courtesy of
Janet & Brian Day

▪ 4½in (12cm)	"WG3"	$350
▪ 5¾in (15cm)	No. 99/54	$450

A very rare model representing Fanny Elssler has jointed arms and elbows which are able to bend because they are attached with elastic cord.

▪ 6in (15cm)	No. 9954	$2250

TOP LEFT & TOP RIGHT: Jenny Lind is another favorite F. & W. Goebel half-doll. The Biedermeier model shown TOP LEFT looks very similar to the half-doll representing Fanny Elssler. She has a similar top-knot of hair, a hair band and her hair was molded in long ringlets. She was made in both nude and clothed (bodice) models. The clothed model has the rose decals of the Biedermeier series and has her face looking downward with two fingers toward her chin. Jenny Lind is also shown as a nude half-doll in the illustration TOP RIGHT.

▪ 3in (8cm)		$385
▪ 4½in (12cm)	"WG3"	$475
▪ 5¾in (15cm)	"WG4"	$575
NUDE:		
▪ 4in (10cm)	"WG3"	$410
▪ 5¾in (15cm)	"WG4"	$520

BOTTOM RIGHT: Napoleon Bonaparte's wife Josephine was the subject of a collectible F. & W. Goebel half-doll. Her hair is trimmed with molded feathers, which were popular hair ornaments worn in the hairdos of the ladies that from the eighteenth-century French Court. Her eyes look downward and her arms are away from her body, but crossed at the elbows toward her breast.

▪ 6in (15cm)	"WG4"	$575
▪ 6½in (17cm)	No. 1105/5	$625

Photo courtesy of Janet & Brian Day

29

Princess de Lamballe — Marie Thérèse Louise de Savoie-Carignan — was modeled as a nude. She has hair molded as a very full powdered wig with long ringlets as well as molded flowers and a bow in her hair. Her arms are away from her body, with one hand reaching toward her face.

- 3⅞in (10cm)   No. 109 $375

The Princess of Prussia wears her gold crown and is molded with a bodice with detailed painting that resembles embroidery. On her wrist are molded two bracelets of beads.

4¾in (12cm)		$900
6¼in (16cm)	"WG5"	$1250

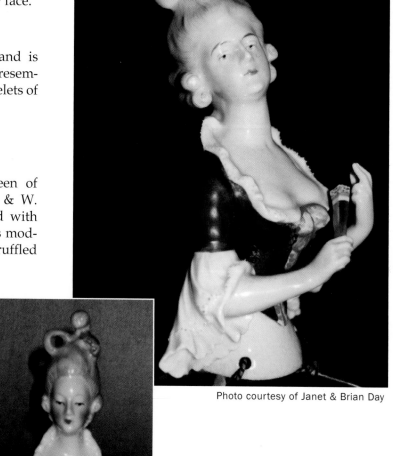

Photo courtesy of Janet & Brian Day

TOP RIGHT: Marie Antoinette became the Queen of France in 1785. As shown in this illustration, F. & W. Goebel depicted her shoulder-length hair molded with three top curls and three colorful feathers. She was modeled clothed, wearing a blue bodice with a white ruffled neckline and holding a fan, and as a nude.

3¼in (8cm)	No. 109	$275
5in (13cm)		$425
NUDE:		
4¾in (12cm)		$325
6in (15cm)	"WG4"	$450
7in (18cm)		$575

MIDDLE: Another model of Marie Antionette has poorer molding. Although modeled with clothing, the beautiful detail seen in the **TOP RIGHT** is missing.

- 4in (10cm)   "BT 1/0" $175

BOTTOM RIGHT: This half-doll is a model of Mrs. Sarah Siddons, a court lady. In this exquisite model, she holds her head in a regal pose and wears her powdered hair in an elegant style graced with three feathers and a bow. Her bodice is light orange in color. The collar is a green shawl topped with a white ruffle and on the edging of the ruffle are tiny dots suggesting embroidery. She wears a locket around her neck and the gold chain is intricately painted. Her face and hands are skillfully painted. She is very rare.

- 6½in (17cm)   "WG*" $860

Number is illegible.

A half-doll of Mademoiselle Camargo was modeled of the dancer Mademoiselle Marie Ann de Cupis de Camargo after the painting by Nicolas Lancret. Her hair is short with a wreath of flowers in it and her arms are outstretched. On the bodice of her dress, flowers are molded in a diagonal pattern starting just under her breast and ending at her waist.

- 3in (8cm) $385

Ladies With Bald Heads
(which require wigs)

RIGHT: F. & W. Goebel made many bald-headed models, each requiring a wig. The original wigs were made of mohair. This lady, with her mask, is called "The Domino." She is attired in the style of the court. A beauty spot is on her cheek.

- 4in (10cm) $625
- 4¾in (12cm)   No. 3401 $670

BELOW & BELOW RIGHT: These models have their arms away from their body, but in various positions. The mold numbers, where they exist, represent different poses.

- 3in (8cm)   "BT455/2/0" $175
- 4in (10cm)   No. 455 $250
- 4in (10cm)   No. 421.3 1/2 $250
- 4¾in (12cm)   "BT410/4/4" $345
- 5in (13cm)   "WG4" $385

A model with the number noted here, holds a mirror in her right hand.

- 5in (13cm)   No. 121.3 $760

Photo courtesy of Janet & Brian Day

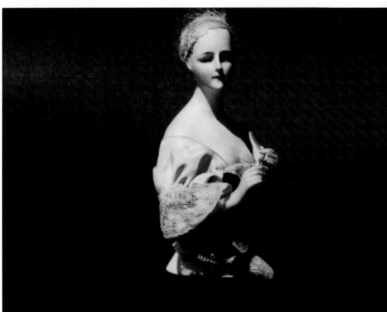

31

Victorian

THE ladies in the eighteenth-century French Court wore powdered wigs with long ringlets. Some F. & W. Goebel half-dolls were designed with similar gray molded wigs. These Victorian models lacked the exquisite detail of the court ladies and the value generally reflects this lack. They were modeled wearing only a camisole, nude or nude and wearing an elaborate large hat. There are various poses with hands away from the body or away and then returning to touch the body.

A nude example with arms away, gracefully bent hands and head tilted with a large embossed base.

5½in (14cm)	No. 320	$560
7in (18cm)	"R.T. 300 5 1/2"	$640

TOP RIGHT: The example shown in Illustration 55 is wearing a camisole with a molded neckline suggesting embroidery. Her powdered hair ends in long ringlets on each side of her neck and her right hand rests above her breast while her left hand is gracefully held away from the body with the palm up. "Germany" and the mold number are embossed on the base.

1¾in (5cm)	No. 180 0/0	$150
3in (8cm)	No. 1806	$225
4in (10cm)	No. 1308.3	$275

A Victorian lady with an original white silk wig, beautifully detailed eyes and arms away from her body.

6in (15cm)	No. 406/6	$385

Colonial Ladies

BOTTOM RIGHT: "Little Lottie," this charming young woman with lovely detailing, wears a beautiful bonnet, fingerless gloves and a locket. She has the familiar rose decals of the Biedermeier models and was made in five sizes. Each size, however diminutive, has the same fine detailing.

2½in (6cm)		$200
3in (8cm)		$310
4in (10cm)	"Bavaria"	$450
4¾in (12cm)		$480
6in (15cm)		$635

LEFT: This model has her gray hair coiled on the top of her head. In her right hand she touches the flower that is placed in her hair near her ear. This half-doll lacks the quality of most F. & W. Goebel figurines.

- 5½in (14cm) $90

Photo courtesy of Gert & Gaby Grollmuss

ABOVE: This beautiful model holds a rose in her right hand and appears to be placing it in her hair. She has two rows of molded beads around her neck and her hair is in long curls at the back of her head.

- 4½in (12cm) $975
- 7½in (19cm)   "B.T. 154" $1100

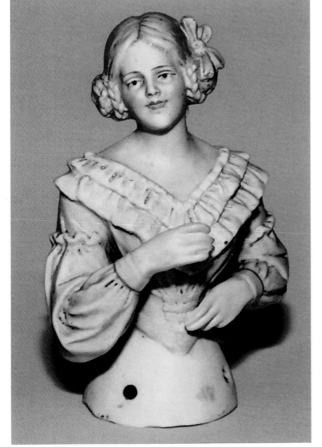

Photo courtesy of Gert & Gaby Grollmuss

LEFT: Here is an exquisite model of a young woman. She has braids coiled around her ears and a placid expression. She was modeled both clothed and nude.

- 4½in (12cm)   "WG 9301" $350

Flappers

An F. & W. Goebel flapper was modeled as a suave Pierrette. Her eyes are either closed or outlined with bottom eyelashes. The Pierrette has the familiar spit curl, while the flapper has her hair molded in the fashionable bob of the time.

- 2½in (6cm)   No. 373 $185
- 6in (15cm)   "ex222" $310

Children

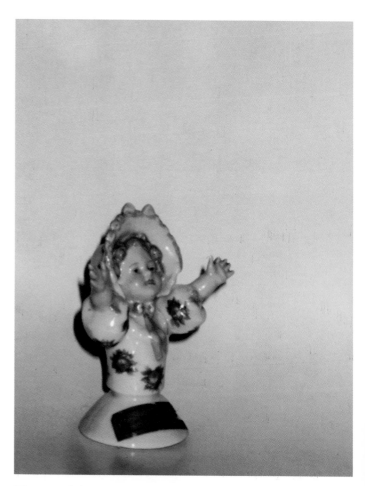

This model was manufactured around the 1950s. Her eyes have a bright-eyed look. She wears a jaunty little hat with her hair in braids and her hands at her sides. Although she was made more recently then the others mentioned previously, she is very difficult to find.

- 3½in (9cm) $190

This model represents a toddler with outstretched arms. She wears her baby bonnet and her clothing has the Biedermeier decals on the bodice. She is very appealing and has the wide base with embossing. On this figure, her "pointer" fingertips are chipped and this damage would decrease the value by thirty percent. The value listed here is for a perfect model.

- 3¾in (10cm)   [Gold Goebel Label] $495

Hertwig & Co.

In 1864, Christoph Hertwig, Johann Nikolaus Beyermann and his son, Benjamin Beyermann, founded Hertwig & Co. in the German town of Kätzhutte. The factory produced a very large number of figurines, Nippes (small porcelain knickknacks) and gift items until it closed in 1990. The Hertwig porcelain factory also made china and bisque doll heads, all-bisque dolls, Tropfenfänger (teapot drip catchers) and Teepuppen (tea-dolls). Some of the half-dolls manufactured were attached to Nadelkissen (pincushions). Each style of half-doll was given a mold number. The plaster molds were numbered sequentially from the largest size to the smallest. Mold numbers are listed under each porcelain object shown in original porcelain factory sample books, which were distributed to wholesalers, as well as on sample boxes containing a number of dolls in varying sizes. (See Appendix C, page 134.)

Some of these half-dolls were of very fine quality and detail, requiring several molds. Others were crudely sculpted, using a two-part mold of just the front and back. Complexity and rarity generally define the price of the object.

Novelty Item
(with a head that bobs)

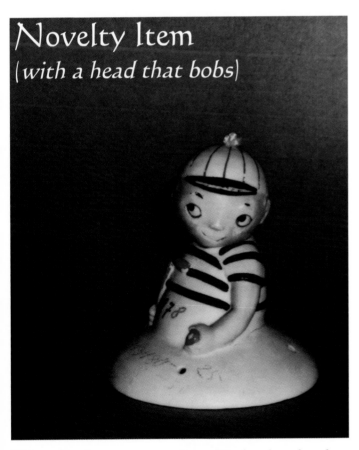

This golfer is a very rare item. His head nods when moved.

- 4in (10cm) No. 2978 $750

Complex Molds With Exquisite Detail

This model has finely sculpted features and is known as the "Flamenco Dancer of Andalusia." She has black hair with a red comb in the manner of a Spanish dancer and wears a gold necklace and armband with a red bracelet on her right arm which extends upward, an inch above her head. Her other arm bends at the level of her neck and away from her body and she holds castanets in her hands.

- 4½in (12cm) No. 6449 $575
- 5½in (14cm) No. 6386 $675
- 6in (15cm) No. 6443 $975

A half-doll posed with arms raised behind her back, leaning forward and wearing a red band with blue feathers, all in bisque and finely painted.

- 3in (8cm) $675
- 4½in (12cm)
  No. 6031 $875+

TOP RIGHT: This half-doll is bisque, with a bald head tilting to the left and eyes glancing sideways in a manner suggesting flirting. Her left arm bends at the elbow with the hand near her breast. Her right arm is raised upwards so her hand is at shoulder level.

- 3in (8cm)
  No. 2420 $175

An all-bisque half-doll with jointed arms, part of the Modern Damenbusten series.

- 4in (10cm)   No. 6078 $395
- 4½in (12cm)   No. 3613 $410

BOTTOM LEFT: This nude model is wearing her original blonde wig. Her arms are away from her body with her hands at the level of her head and turned away from her.

- 2¼in (6cm)   No. 5884 $165

BOTTOM RIGHT: Another model, seen below, has her arms raised toward her shoulders with the elbows elevated. She has black "bobbed" hair and a red hair band. While mold number 5382 is shown here, there are several variations of this model and several similar molds were made.

- 2½in (6cm)   No. 5382 $350

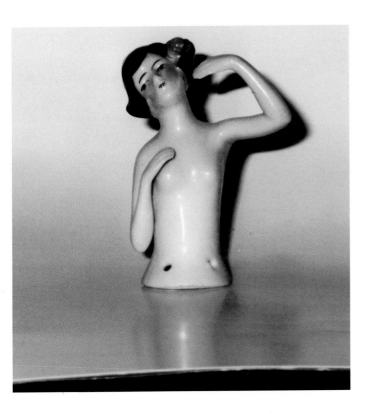

This model is nude. She has her head tilted to the right with a rose on the left side of her head. Her left hand is extended upwards toward the rose, while her right upper arm is parallel to her right side with the lower arm bending upward so that her hand is just above (but not touching) her bust.

- 2½in (6cm)   No. 4339 $155
- 2¾in (7cm)   No. 8036 $215

This colonial woman has shoulder-length black hair. Her poke bonnet, with a wide brim at the top that narrows as it nears her neck, ties with a ribbon. She wears a shawl over her bodice with full sleeves which end with a wide ruffle. Both arms and hands, although away from her body, return close to her front. She points two fingers of her right hand. At times she is found with the left hand molded to her chest, rather than separate. The model of the same figure can vary in the quality of the painting, and thus, the value.

- 2½in (6cm)   Nos. 5280, 5289 $40 – $68

Complex Models With Arms Away
(without illustrations)

- 2½in (6cm)   Nos. 7747, 7744, 7743, 7741, $300 – $450
             7740, 7398, 7396 — depending
             upon complexity of mold

Holding Objects

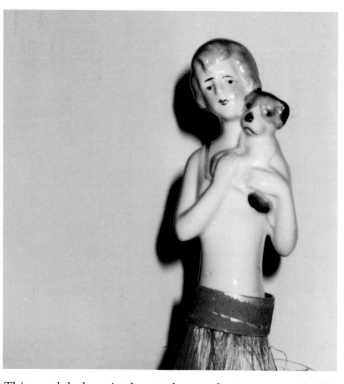

This model, done in the art deco style, is a woman holding a puppy.
- 4in (10cm)   No. 7042 $575

A flapper holding a mirror.
- 3½in (9cm)   No. 7043 $525

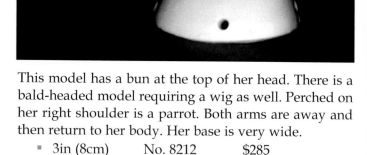

This model has a bun at the top of her head. There is a bald-headed model requiring a wig as well. Perched on her right shoulder is a parrot. Both arms are away and then return to her body. Her base is very wide.
- 3in (8cm)   No. 8212 $285

A mother holding a baby.
- 3½in (9cm) $625

Complex Molds with Both Arms Away from Body and Returning

- 2½in (6cm)   Nos. 7662, 7663, 7664, 7665 $250
- 3in (8cm)   Nos. 7645, 7646, 7647, 7648 $300

Models With One Arm Touching Body, One Arm Away

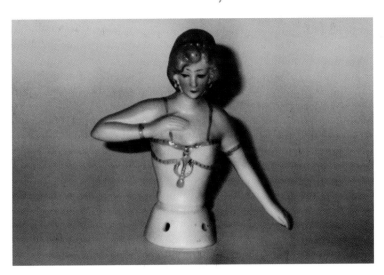

This bisque model wears green beads in her blonde hair and faces toward the right. Her left hand touches the strap of her dress while her left arm is held away in an unbending fashion. The bodice of her dress is trimmed in green, in a manner that represents braid. She has finely sculpted facial features.

- 2¾in (7cm)   No. 5493 $125

Both Arms Away, Then Returning to Body

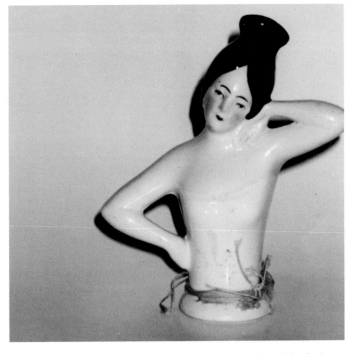

This woman is wearing a Dutch hat that is white with blue polka dots and a white blouse with a blue collar. She is skillfully sculpted and the painting of her facial features and her clothing is well done.

- 4in (10cm)   No. 8874 $275

This commonly found Spanish woman has black hair decorated with a molded comb. The combs were painted in a variety of colors, including red, blue and yellow.

2½in (6cm)	No. 5175	$33
2¾in (7cm)	Nos. 8037, 4355	$35
3in (8cm)	No. 5826	$40
3in (8cm)	No. 5063	$40
3½in (9cm)	No. 4347	$45
4in (10cm)	No. 8033	$50

TOP LEFT: This flapper is wearing a red and white wide-brimmed hat and a blue blouse with a wide yellow collar.

- 4in (10cm) $125

ABOVE: This flapper is wearing a yellow hat with yellow feathers. Both of her arms are away and returning. In her right hand, she holds a fan with ostrich feathers.

3½in (9cm)	No. 8026	$105
3¾in (10cm)	No. 7046	$115
4in (10cm)	No. 7946	$135

BOTTOM LEFT: This woman is a popular model. She may represent a swimmer or a lady in a strapless gown. One hand touches her hair while the other rests at her chest.

- 3¾in (10cm)   No. 6237 $80

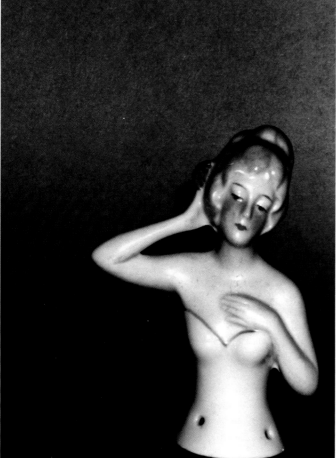

This woman with blonde hair is wearing a yellow cap with a band and two roses on each side. She has a tie around her neck and her left hand holds the tie while the right hand is at her waist.

▪ 1½in (4cm)	No. 4183	$65
▪ 2½in (6cm)		$70
▪ 3in (8cm)	No. 5160	$78

This woman is wearing a red hat with her head tilted to the right and holding a fan in her left hand.

▪ 2½in (6cm)	No. 5125	$85
▪ 3in (8cm)	Nos. 6037, 4351, 5582	$95
▪ 3½in (9cm)	No. 4345	$100
▪ 3¾in (10cm)	No. 8050	$125
▪ 4in (10cm)	No. 4345	$145

LEFT: This woman with bobbed hair is wearing a sleeveless pink blouse.

▪ 3½in (9cm)	No. 2348	$145
▪ 4in (10cm)		$165

RIGHT: This woman has two molded feathers in her shoulder-length hair. She has a series of ring-shaped barrettes on the right side of her hair and her hands are touching the curls on her left side. She wears a bodice that has a "V" shaped neckline. Her sleeves have very wide ruffles ending slightly above her elbow.

▪ 2½in (6cm)	
Nos. 5626, 4354	$75
▪ 3¼in (8cm)	
No. 5543	$85

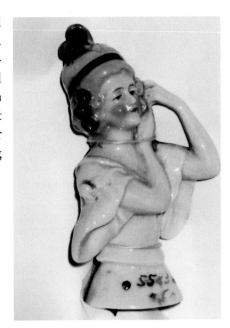

Simple Two-Piece Molds

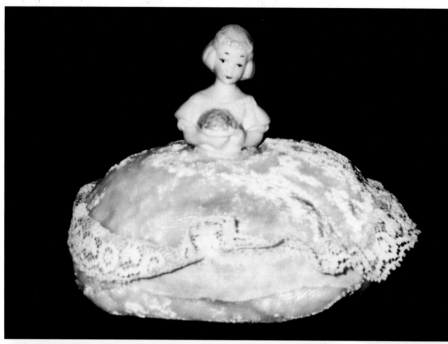

This young child holds a bouquet of flowers in her right arm with her left hand touching the right one.

- 1½in (4cm) $95

This flapper has black hair and wears a blue headband with a yellow feather. Her arms are next to her body and she holds a flower in her hand. This mold is very common.

2in (5cm)	No. 5333	$45
3½in (9cm)		$55

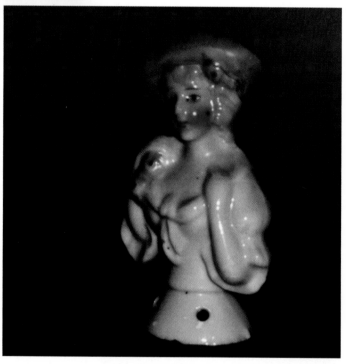

This woman is wearing a hat with a large brim, with two roses under the brim on the left side of her hair. She also wears a blouse with a scoop neckline that ties in the front. Her arms and body are one piece. The flowers on her dress are just below the right hand resting on her shoulder.

2½in (6cm)	No. 5624	$50
2¾in (7cm)	No. 4354	$55
3in (8cm)	No. 5581	$68
3½in (9cm)	No. 4349	$80

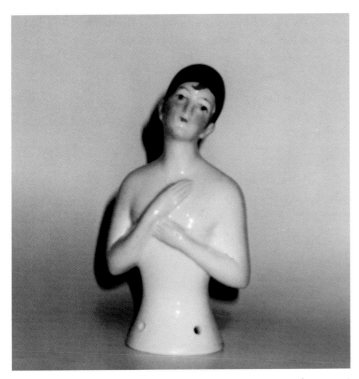

This Pierrot has both arms next to his body, clasped over his chest. His head, with three red "spit" curls, is tilted and he is wearing a black skullcap.

▪ 2¾in (7cm)	No. 4356	$95
▪ 3in (8cm)	No. 4353	$105
▪ 3¼in (8cm)	No. 6512	$110
▪ 3½in (9cm)	No. 5580	$145
▪ 3¾in (10cm)	No. 4348	$120
▪ 4in (10cm)	No. 8034	$145

This woman with brown ringlets is wearing a frilly blouse that falls over her shoulders. Her arms are clasped in front and her head is tilted to the right.

▪ 2½in (6cm)	No. 2623 or No. 3623*	$60
▪ 3in (8cm)	No. 5580	$70
▪ 3¼in (8cm)	No. 6512	$80

Number is illegible.

Frequently Found Models

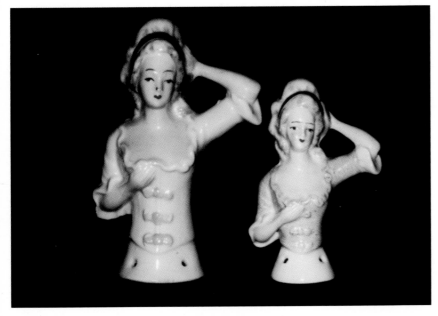

In these models, a woman with one hand to her hair and one hand to her breast.

▪ 2½in (6cm)	No. 4350	$40
▪ 3in (8cm)	No. 6347	$45
▪ 3¼in (8cm)	No. 8030	$50
▪ 3½in (9cm)	No. 5023	$50
▪ 3¾in (10cm)	No. 4344	$55
▪ 3¾in (10cm)	No. 6342	$55
▪ 4in (10cm)		$65

This lady wears a sleeveless dress and has a blue ribbon in her long hair. One hand rests at her bosom, the other at her waistline.

2in (5cm)	No. 5559	$40
2½in (6cm)	No. 5501	$45
2¾in (7cm)	No. 4352	$50
3in (8cm)	No. 4346	$50
3in (8cm)	No. 5509	$50
3¾in (10cm)	No. 8032	$60

Unmarked and Complex Mold

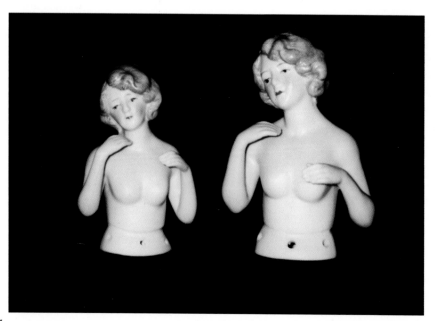

This example is an unmarked blonde half-doll of very fine quality, with arms away from her body. She does not carry a mold number but through recent research, she has been identified as a product of Hertwig & Co.

2½in (6cm)	$125
3in (8cm)	$145

Japanese

Many half-dolls were produced in Japan for sale in Europe and the United States. The production began around World War I and continued well into the 1950s. These dolls were produced from copies of German half-dolls. Generally, these models lack the crispness of the German counterpart. The clay that was used does not have the translucence of that used for the German dolls, and the painting lacks detail.

The earliest half-dolls produced in Japan were stamped "Nippon" to indicate Japan as the country of origin. Half-dolls marked "Nippon" are generally difficult to find and rare. After 1921, Japanese porcelain and china items carried the name of the manufacturer, such as Noritake, Morimuri and eventually Shackman. Shackman produced half-dolls beginning in the second half of the twentieth century.

Most Japanese dolls that are commonly found now have "Made in Japan" printed on the base or inside the model. There are a few half-dolls that carry a mold number, but the majority of half-dolls do not.

Complicated Model Requiring Multiple Molds

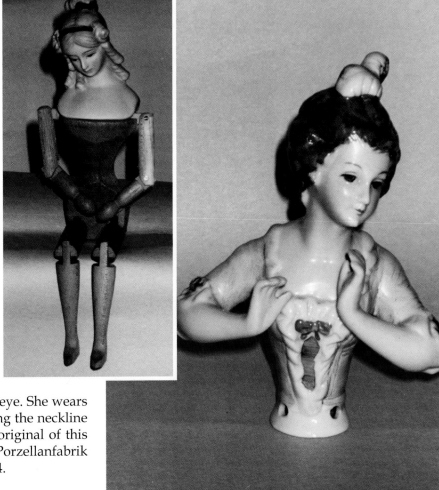

NEAR RIGHT: Shackman half-dolls were made for a company in New York around 1970. F. & W. Goebel modeled a half-doll using Jenny Lind as a model and the Shackman Company copied her. This Shackman Company model has a bisque head and shoulder plate ending just above the chest and was sold attached to a wooden jointed body. The features are crisp and the painting of this model is well done.

- 3¼in (8cm) $40

FAR RIGHT: This Shackman model has been sold as a German antique many times. This is a case of "buyer beware." The value of the Shackman model is much lower than the corresponding German antique model. However, both models have the same crisp modeling, although the antique model is more pronounced and slightly taller. She wears her brown hair in an updo and has feathers at the top of her head. Her eyes have a red line over each eye. She wears a pink dress with a yellow ruffle accenting the neckline and continuing down to the waist. The original of this model was made by the Sitzendorfer Porzellanfabrik and should carry the mold number 21634.

- 5in (13cm) $50

RIGHT: This half-doll is finely sculpted and painted. She could easily be taken for one of German origin except for the mark "Nippon" on her base. She is dressed to visit or promenade, as she wears her "lamp-shade" hat and gloves. She is also wearing a blouse with a low-cut neckline over which she wears a laced vest. She does not have a mold number.

- 4in (10cm) $160

Holding Objects

BELOW: This model is a sweet child with her arms full of colorful balls.

- 3in (8cm) $125
- 3½in (9cm) $140

Simple Two-Part Models

BELOW: This model is commonly found in several sizes. Her head is tilted to the left and she has short curly hair. Her arms are away from her body but return so that her hands rest on her hips. She wears a simple dress with a rose at her shoulder.

- 3¾in (10cm) $40

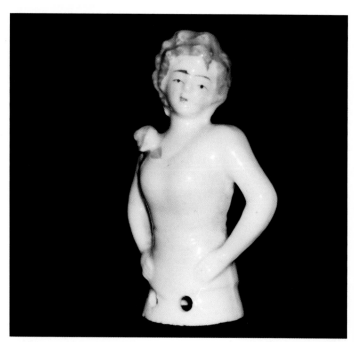

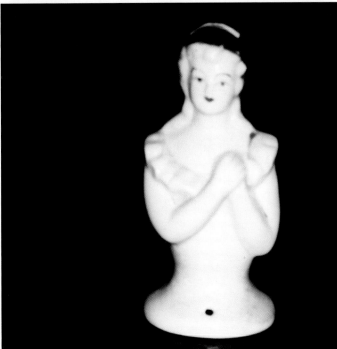

LEFT: This blonde model is similar to the figure shown in the bottom right illustration on the previous PAGE. Her hands rest at her waist but she lacks the rose on her shoulder.

- 3½in (9cm) $40

BELOW: This model is found in several sizes. She wears a hat with a wide flat brim that rests at the top of her head. Her right hand touches the brim and her left hand rests at her waist. She wears a dress with a shawl collar.

- 2¾in (7cm) $35
- 3½in (9cm) $50

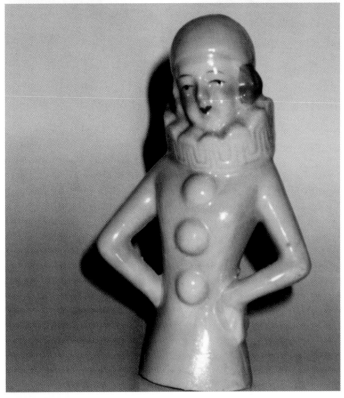

ABOVE: This model wears a pink band in her black hair. Her head looks downward and her hands are clasped at her left shoulder. She wears a pink dress with a ruffle at the neckline.

- 3¼in (8cm) $40

RIGHT: This clown is a copy of a Gebrüder Heubach half-doll. He wears a yellow outfit and a yellow skull-cap with a white ruffle about his neck. His hands are at his waist. He is well made and, without his "Made in Japan" mark, he could easily pass as his German counterpart.

- 3½in (9cm) $85

Carl Schneider

The Gräfenthal porcelain factory — Unger, Schneider & Hutschenreuther — was founded in 1861. This factory was the forerunner of the Carl* Schneider porcelain factory. In 1885, Carl Schneider died and the name of the porcelain factory became Carl Schneider's Erben (Heirs). The factory closed in 1974.

The Carl Schneider factory produced a variety of porcelain products, including half-dolls. The half-dolls were sculpted and painted in the factory. They

*In German, "Carl" is spelled "Karl" and it appears both ways in references. Here the spelling "Carl" will be used.

were generally marked with the Schneider trademark, "DEP" and a mold number ranging from 10,000 to 20,000. This factory was one of the largest producers of half-dolls. Examples are found in the majority of half-doll collections. The half-dolls tend to be reasonably priced with the exception of a few that were sculpted with intricate details.

The examples shown here are accompanied with the mold numbers of other similar models that would be valued similarly to that shown in the illustration.

The mold numbers are for those dolls that are beautifully painted, with arms away from their body and nude, so the owner (or factory) could supply the pincushion (nadelkissen).

LEFT: This model is a dark-haired flapper with her arms extended. She wears only her jewelry consisting of earrings, bracelets and a necklace. The fingers on her hands are well defined. The model is a very graceful young woman.

- 4in (10cm)　　No. 13475　　$300
- 4¾in (12cm)　No. 17039　　$425

RIGHT: This beautiful art deco lady wears a gold band across her forehead. Her red earrings dangle from the lobe of her ear. She has heavy eye makeup. Her arms are fully extended away from her body and the fingers on her hand are gracefully posed. Her right arm extends upward, while the left is lowered, suggesting a pose of a dancer. Although she is nude, she wears a gold bracelet on her upper right arm and a red one on her right wrist.

- 3¾in by 7½in (10cm by 19cm)
  No. --- 08*　　$525

Missing numbers are illegible.

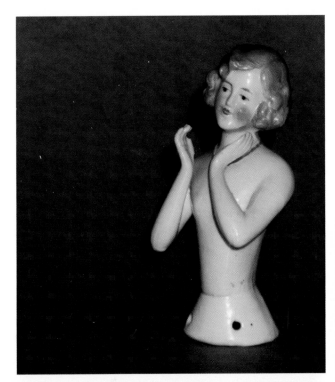

LEFT: This lovely flapper has her arms extended upward and her hands extended out and toward her face. She is nude, except for her necklace. Her hands are meticulously sculpted and have fine detailing, as do the features of her face.

- 4in (10cm)   No. 14377 $495

BELOW: This blonde woman, with feathers and beads in her hair, holds a mirror.

- 4½in (12cm)   No. 13910 $275

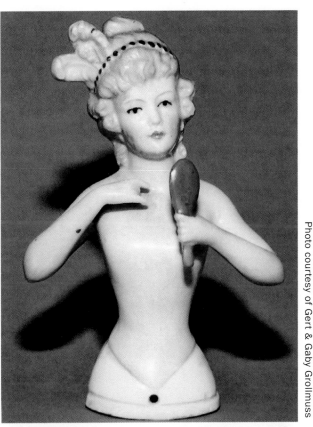

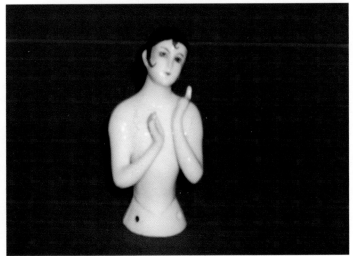

ABOVE: This Pierrette has one hand pointing toward her ear.

2¼in (6cm)	No. 14267	$225
3in (8cm)	No. 14266	$275
4½in (12cm)	No. 14264	$350

A Pierrette with arms slightly different from the one shown in the illustration directly **ABOVE**.

- 4in (10cm)   No. 14605 $310

RIGHT: This beautiful flapper wears a red headband in her hair. Her right hand is raised and tilted toward her face. The left hand is placed diagonally across her front with her hands tilted downward. She is a figure of grace and beauty.

- 4¾in (12cm)   No. 14991 $470

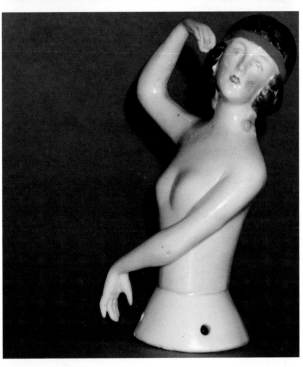

A half-doll resembling a lady in the eighteenth-century French Court with powdered hair and holding a letter to her face.

- 4¼in (11cm)   No. 14389 $214

LEFT: This Victorian woman is very similar to figurines made by other manufacturers. Her arms, away from her body, end with her hands at chest level.

- 3¾in (10cm)   No. 14754 $195

BELOW: This woman with flowers in her hair has her arms extended toward her chest and chin. Her hair can be silver or blonde.

- 3½in (9cm)   No. 15278 $185
- 4in (10cm)   No. 15273 $165
- 5in (13cm)   No. 15272 $225

A woman, very similar to the one shown in the illustration **BELOW**, but without flowers in her hair.

- 2½in (6cm)   No. 14277 $165
- 3in (8cm)   No. 14275 $175
- 4¾in (12cm)   No. 14274 $183

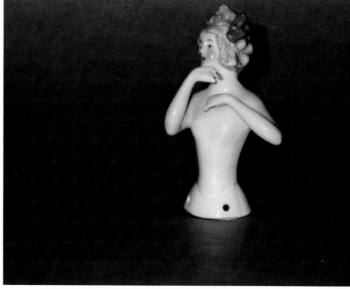

LEFT: This whimsical model wears nothing but an array of large flowers and leaves in her hair. The placement of her arms suggests she might be dancing.

- 4¼in (11cm)   No. 14980 $315
- 5¾in (15cm)   No. 14979 $460

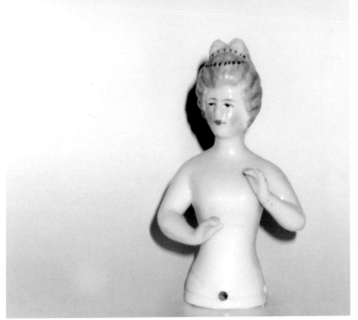

ABOVE: A woman with a powdered coiffure wears two rows of beads in her hair with her arms extended in front of her body.

- 4¾in (12cm)   No. 13911 $105

A model similar to the one shown **ABOVE**, but with her arms bent at the elbows and hands above her chest.

- 3in (8cm)   No. 13945 $135

Other examples:

3½in (9cm)	No. 10041	$155
4in (10cm)	No. 14756	$125
4¾in (12cm)	No. 14753	$135
6in (15cm)	No. 13268	$365

This woman with powdered hair has a huge curl piled at the top of her head. The mold numbers listed here have the same hairdo, but the arms might be molded in different positions. All of these examples are nude.

3in (8cm)	No. 12762	$115
3½in (9cm)	No. 12763	$125
4in (10cm)	No. 13952	$165
4¾in (12cm)	No. 12756	$170
5½in (14cm)	No. 11133	$190*
6½in (17cm)	No. 13268	$185

In this example the arms are extended.

Wearing Clothing, with Arms Extended

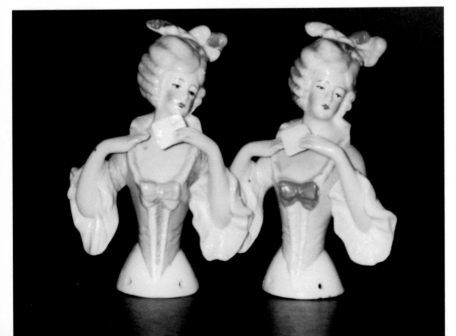

These lovely young women, with feathers in their hair, are the same model. Each is holding a letter towards her face. Their identical Victorian dresses are painted in different colors.

2¾in (7cm)	No. 14391	$165
3¼in (8cm)	No. 14284	$195
3¾in (10cm)	No. 14389	$235
4¼in (11cm)	No. 14281	$250

Arms Extended, Then Returning to Body; Detailed and May Hold Objects

LEFT: This half-doll, with beads and flowers in her hair, is holding a fan. The hand-painted flowers trim her sleeve. She is similar to the half-doll shown on PAGE 49, top illustration in the right column (blue background).

- 2in (5cm)   No. 14968 $115
- 3¾in (10cm)   No. 12286 $195
- 4in (10cm)   No. 11937 $255

BELOW: This figurine appears to be a version of Mrs. Sarah Siddons. She wears a shawl collar that ties at the end and a hair band in her powdered hair of long ringlets. The sleeves to the dress are very narrow, ending with a ruffle at the wrist. An F. & W. Goebel model (seen on PAGE 30, bottom illustration) has greater detail and the hands are different, as is the direction of the face. However, both half-dolls are so similar that it seems that this model was sculpted after a portrait.

- 5in (13cm)   No. 15142 $185

ABOVE: This half-doll wears a very fancy hat. Her full sleeves have hand-painted flowers and she has gold trim on her bodice.

- 3¼in (8cm)   No. 17243 $95

TOP RIGHT: This half-doll wears a fancy hat placed at the left side of her head. Her hair is in ringlets. She wears a double necklace. One hand touches her hair and one her shoulder.

- 2½in (6cm)   No. 19098 $95

BELOW: This half-doll wears a little hat which is perched on the right side of her head. Peeking out from under her hat is a ribbon. Her drop-shouldered dress is trimmed with a molded bow and she holds her fan tilting downward from her waist.

- 3in (8cm)   No. 18001 $95

BOTTOM RIGHT: This flapper wears a cloche and a coat with an ermine fur collar. Her arms are extended and her left hand touches the side of her hat while the right holds a purse.

- 4in (10cm)   No. 14506 $155

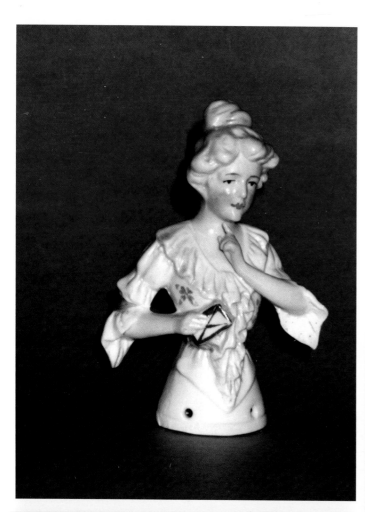

- 4in (10cm)   No. 13420 $185

A lady similar to the half-doll seen on the **LEFT**, except that she wears a bonnet, holds her purse in her right hand while the other hand holds a fan.

- 3½in (9cm)   No. 12287 $150

BELOW: This half-doll has an elegant hairdo with two rows of beads in her hair. She holds a fan to her right ear and a flower in her left hand.

- 3¾in (10cm)   No. 12736 $195
- 4½in (12cm)   No. 13911 $235

BOTTOM LEFT: This colonial lady wears a bonnet and her hands extend out and back to her waist.

- 4in (10cm)   No. 14504 $85
- 4¼in (11cm)   No. 14505 $95

One Hand Extended, One Arm Close or Touching Body

A half-doll representing Lady Hamilton, Lord Nelson's mistress, has one arm molded away from her body while the other is touching the flower in her hair.

- 6in (15cm)   No. 16952 $350

A young girl dressed in a green blouse has a scarf draped around her neck and falling to her waist where it is tucked into her belt.

- 3½in (9cm)   No. 14178 $165

RIGHT: This Dutch woman wears a white blouse with a blue corset laced in front. She holds a ball of yarn in her right hand and the left arm holds the yarn.

2¾in (7cm)		$165
3¼in (8cm)		$185
4in (10cm)		$200
4¼in (11cm)	No. 12527	$225

BELOW: This woman, in a French dress, wears a gold cross at her neck and a shawl around her shoulders.

- 3⅜in (9cm)   No. 14416 $250

ABOVE: The very popular model of a Spanish lady in her lacy mantilla has exceptional beauty. She wears a dark red bodice with roses at the waist. Her right hand is placed close to her breast while the left is at her waist.

- 6¼in (16cm)   No. 10016 $915

Photo courtesy of Gert & Gaby Grollmuss

55

Less Complicated Molds, Some Detailed

TOP LEFT: This Victorian woman has her arms against her body. She wears a blue band in her powdered hair and ruffles adorn the end of her sleeves and the front of her blue and pink bodice.

- 2¾in (7cm)   No. 13016 $125

BELOW LEFT: This half-doll is somewhat difficult to find but very popular among collectors. She holds her tennis racket in her hands and wears a large scarf tied with a bow on her hair.

- 4¼in (11cm)   No. 14508 $285

BELOW RIGHT: This lovely half-doll holds a basket. She has ringlets in her hair and wears her little kerchief bonnet.

- 3¾in (10cm)   No. 13752 $185

Photo courtesy of Gert & Gaby Grollmuss

TOP RIGHT: This young woman has a bow on top of her powdered hair. Her arms are close to her body with her hands resting at her breast. She is dressed all in white except for pink roses that are slightly below her waist.

- 3½in (9cm)   No. 15508 $50

BELOW: This woman is very similar to the model shown **BELOW RIGHT**. She holds a bouquet of orange flowers in her right arm while her left hand rests near the hand with the flowers. She wears a bonnet over her long curls and a pink shawl over her green dress.

- 3½in (9cm)   No. 14686 $85

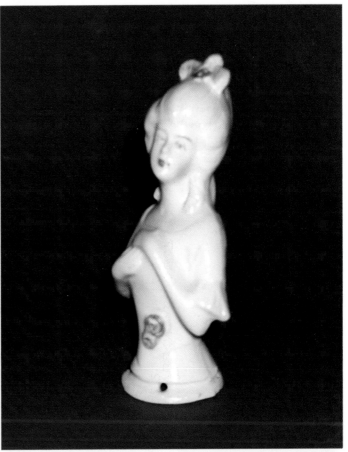

BELOW RIGHT: This woman holds her bouquet of flowers in her right arm while the left hand touches the stems. She is wearing a large hat adorned with a very large bow. Her green dress has a pink shawl collar.

- 4¼in (11cm)   No. 13704 $95

TOP RIGHT: This child is in a Mardi Gras costume. She is a very small size, but charming.

- 2½in (6cm)   No. 14802 $110

BELOW: This figurine is actually a bell. Inside the hollow of her skirt is the Carl Schneider mark. She is included because she has the same facial features and the hairstyle as the half-doll seen in the illustration on the **TOP RIGHT**.

- 6in (15cm) $55

BOTTOM RIGHT: This half-doll is an inexpensive model which is also frequently found as a Japanese model (see PAGE 47, top illustration in the right-hand column). The model's left hand holds the upper brim of her hat while the right hand rests at her waist. She wears an outfit with a shawl collar.

- 4in (10cm)   No. 14503 $70

Sitzendorfer Porzellanfabrik

In 1760, Georg Heinrich Macheleid was granted permission to produce porcelain in Sitzendorf by Prince Johann Friedrich von Schwarzburg. The factory then moved to Volkstedt in 1762. However, in 1850, Wilhelm Liebmann was granted permission to manufacture porcelain and reestablished a porcelain factory in Sitzendorf. In 1858, a fire destroyed all but the ovens. The premises were well insured so the factory was built up again and production continued under the direction of Alfred and Carl Wilhelm Voigt.

In 1879, the brothers Voigt became partners in the factory and, in 1881, changed the name of the factory to the Gebrüder Voigt porcelain factory. In 1896, the name was changed again to "Sitzendorfer Porzellanfabrik, formerly Alfred Voigt" (sole owner from 1911 to 1922). From 1872 to the present time, the factory has used the name: "Sitzendorf Porcelain Factory" when conducting business with English speaking countries.

From 1887 until 1990, the Voigts used a trademark featuring several designs of crossed lines. From 1902 until the present, the factory has used two designs of an ornate crown over an "S" as the factory trademark. The factory has not duplicated the puff figures, perfume containers and half-dolls produced from 1926 to 1940. These items are rare and valued by collectors who appreciate their beautiful sculpting. The puff dishes have their values listed in the section about puff dishes and the bases for powder dishes.

Some of the half-dolls are difficult to identify. Many do not have a clear company mark but are marked with the numbering system illustrated in an old catalog with figures numbered beginning with 22,000. The quality of these half-dolls is exceptional. The sculpting is sharp, both in the facial features and the beautifully detailed and expressive hands.

Mademoiselle Camargo
(Mademoiselle Marie Ann de Cupis de Camargo)

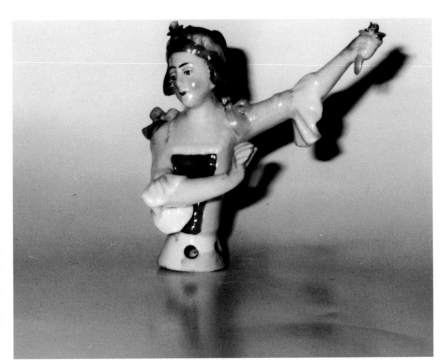

This half-doll is very similar to those representing Madamoiselle Camargo. This mold was made with the woman holding a mirror, as well as a rose. When roses are applied by hand rather than molded, the process is called Dresden. This Dresden rose retains all its petals. The facial features and fingers are very delicate and skillfully painted.

2¾in (7cm)	No. 22179	$185
2½in (6cm)	No. 22473	$175
2¾in (7cm)	No. 22479	$240

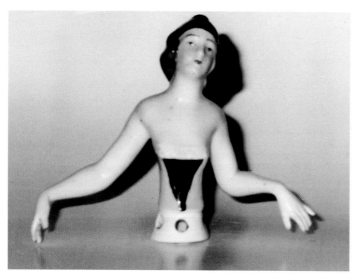

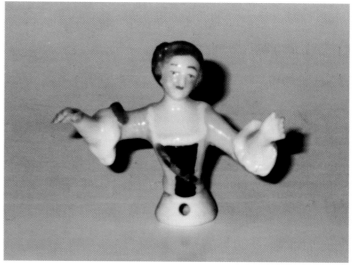

This small model has her arms gracefully placed away from her body. The tiny fingers show individual modeling. Her face is beautiful and she wears a black band in her hair that matches the black detail on her bodice.

- 2¼in (6cm)   No. 22670 $165

This half-doll was inspired by Mademoiselle Camargo, and she has outstretched arms and a diagonal band representing a string of flowers on her bodice. The facial features are skillfully painted. Her tiny hands are beautifully detailed with fingers molded individually.

- 1¾in (5cm)   No. 22871 $145

Victorian Women

A beautiful nude Victorian woman holds a letter to her chest. The facial features and hands are very typical of the Sitzendorfer Porzellanfabrik figurines. Her gray hair has individual strokes and her head is tilted to the right. Her arms, bent at the elbow, are held towards her chest.

- 3in (8cm)   No. 24699 $225
- 5in (13cm)   No. 22854 $390

RIGHT: This lady has her brown hair in a bun at the top of her head. Other half-dolls of this same model have been painted with gray or blonde hair. The hair is painted with strokes that give the appearance of individual strands. She has a blue band in her hair and her head tilts to the right. Her right arm is gracefully held at hip level, while the left is bent upward. Both hands are molded as though to hold an object. This half-doll is beautifully sculpted and painted.

- 2½in (6cm)   No. 23008 $190
- 3in (8cm)   No. 23007 $225
- 3¾in (10cm)   No. 22674 $295
- 5¼in (13cm)   No. 23146 $425

A mold similar to the one shown on the RIGHT has blonde hair. The head and bodice are the same mold. The positions of both arms, however, are held in a higher position.

- 3½in (9cm)   No. 22674 $250

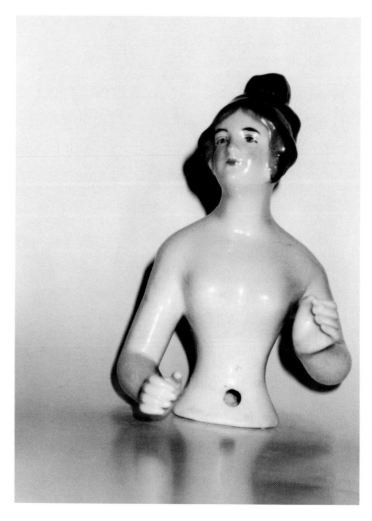

RIGHT: This nude model has hair that is molded into a casual bun with gold beads as decoration. Her face is skillfully molded and very expressive. Her head turns to the left and her beautiful arms are raised upward.

- 3¾in (10cm)   No. 22205 $260
- 3¾in (10cm)   No. 22206 $290

A very delicate mold, with her head tilted to the right, has hair topped with roses and a braid around her head at her forehead. Her arms are held upward towards the left and she is nude.

- 2½in (6cm)   No. 22614 $165

A model, dressed in a blue bodice with red bows on her sleeves, has blonde hair with feathers decorating the hairdo. Her head is tilted downward and she holds a lorgnette.

- 3¾in (10cm)   No. 22549 $190

A model with blonde hair combed upward has her arms held towards her shoulders. She wears a maroon blouse over another with long full white sleeves. The low-cut dress has a green collar.

- 2¾in (7cm)   No. 23435 $165

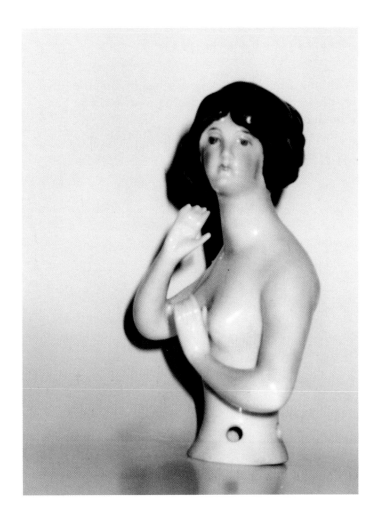

An Important Comparison

THIS half-doll is almost identical to a half-doll made by a Japanese company for Shackman of New York from this model. The Shackman figure is skillfully painted and, if it lost the paper label, it could be sold as a vintage Sitzendorfer Porzellanfabrik product. The difference between the manufactured products is that a number is embossed on the back of the base of the Sitzendorfer Porzellanfabrik model while the Shackman model has none. In some of the Sitzendorfer Porzellanfabrik half-dolls, the numbers are faint but can be detected with a magnifying glass. Unless there is evidence of numbering on the base, the model should be considered a Shackman. The figures shown on the **LEFT** are Sitzendorfer Porzellanfabrik models.

This eighteenth-century court lady is a nude, although the same half-doll has been sculpted with clothing. She wears molded feathers in her "powdered" hair, as was the style then. Both of her beautiful hands reach upward toward her face, but remain separated from her head. Her head is tilted to the side and her face has delicate features and is very expressive.

- 3½in (9cm)   No. 21275 $275
- 4¼in (11cm)   No. 21276 $290

WITH CLOTHING:

- 4½in (12cm)   No. 21634 $290

Young Woman

With one arm raised above her head while the other is at her chest, this lovely young nude woman has a wreath of flowers in her hair.

- 2¾in (7cm)   No. 22687 $190

Flappers

Photo courtesy of Norma Smith

This little flapper wears her cloche hat that ends just above her eyes which have heavy eye makeup. She wears gold earrings. Her right arm extends upward and holds a flower with her right hand touching her shoulder. The left arm bends at the elbow so that her hand rests at the waist. Her green bodice is trimmed with purple.

- 3¼in (8cm)   No. 27442 $185

This figure was made from a two-piece mold. The half-doll has marvelous detail and the pose is wonderful. This half-doll's chin rests on her hands as she looks outward. She wears a yellow comb in her black hair. Her bodice is yellow with black fringe painted on as though falling off her shoulders. Both sizes of this half-doll have same mold number — 22721 — but above the mold number is another number that is related to the size.

- 3½in (9cm)   No. 22721 $180
- 6½in (17cm)   No. 22721 $435

Weiss, Kühnert & Co.

The porcelain factory of Weiss, Kühnert & Co. was built in Gräfenthal, Thuringia, in Germany around 1891 and initially manufactured doll heads. However, a page from a 1924 catalog illustrates one hundred fifty models of half-dolls. The catalog page is an important piece of research information as the Weiss, Kühnert & Co. half-dolls are very similar to those of the Hertwig & Co. factory both in modeling as well as in the four number system. The half-dolls were made in three or four sizes of each mold with the largest at 4in (10cm) to 4½in (12cm) and the smallest at 2¼in (6cm). The largest model of a grouping carries the smallest mold number. The molds vary from the simple two-piece molds, (as mold No. 6087) to the complex model with arms away from the body and requiring several molds (No. 5564). The only identifying features are the known mold numbers. A very few are marked "W.K.C."

In 1998, the old factory was purchased by Susan Bickert and Roland Schlegel and renamed the German Doll Company. According to Susan, who provided the history of Weiss, Kühnert & Co., "The Weiss, Kühnert & Co. factory…made figural porcelain (or figurines, half-dolls, egg timers, powder boxes and other items) until 1933. The factory remained open and continued to produce, but it was wartime in Germany and the factory turned to making dishes for the war effort (plates, cups and saucers). After the war, the factory continued production, but the Communists took over the factory and forced the Weiss family out. The company produced beer steins, bowls and some animal figurines. Then, in 1991, the factory closed."

Arms Away From Body, Hands Not Touching

LEFT: This model is beautifully detailed and her face is lovely. The lavender band in her hair matches the trim on her bodice and there is a slight tilt of her head to the left. Her arms, which bend at the elbow, are raised.

2in (5cm)	No. 5556	$130
2¾in (7cm)	No. 5555	$135
3⅛in (8cm)	No. 5554	$145
3½in (9cm)	No. 5553	$160

The Gainsborough hat worn by this model is exquisite, but aside from the hat, she is nude. Her face is well painted and she raises her arms above her waist, which is very small, as is her base.

2in (5cm)	No. 5666	$160
3in (8cm)	No. 5665	$185
4in (10cm)	No. 5664	$215

Arms Away, But Returning to Body

TOP LEFT: This half-doll tops a little broom. Her hair is molded in ringlets and her arms bend at the elbows and return to her bodice. She holds flowers whose stems extend below her hands. This specific model lacks detail which is reflected in the value.

- 4in (10cm)   No. 5596 $80

The same Victorian model mold as seen on the **LEFT** with the sculpting and painting skillfully done would have a higher value.

- 4in (10cm)   No. 5596 $105

BELOW: This lady, dressed in red with navy trim, has a navy bow in her blonde hair. However, the hair and clothing differs from model to model of this same mold. One hand rests at her chest and the other at the front of her waist. The molding and painting of her facial features is not well done.

2½in (6cm)	No. 5561	$80
3in (8cm)	No. 5559	$70
3½in (9cm)	No. 5501	$55

BOTTOM LEFT: This little Dutch child is a very charming model. She wears her blue hat over blonde curls. Her little right index finger points upward while her other hand holds a bouquet of flowers.

2½in (6cm)	No. 5719	$85
3¾in (10cm)	No. 6348	$70

Photo courtesy of Norma Smith

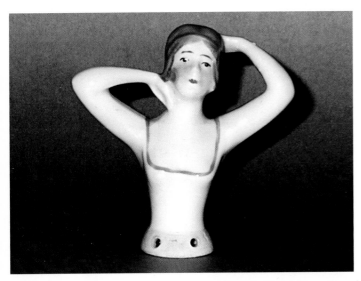

This model has been painted with brown, blonde and black hair cut in a flapper bob and topped with a hair band. The facial painting is well done and the features pleasant but the detail of her clothing is unclear. The right hand rests at her throat, the left at the back of her head.

2¼in (6cm)	No. 6104	$55
2¾in (7cm)	No. 6103	$65
3¼in (8cm)	No. 6102	$75

This is the same model as seen LEFT, but with a dark red band in her hair. She is almost identical to a model made by Hertwig & Co. with mold number 4192. The only difference between the half-dolls is that the left hand on the Weiss, Kühnert & Co. model reaches to the top of the head while the left hand of the Hertwig & Co. model reaches to touch the half-doll's back.

This well made half-doll has arms which bend at the elbow and return with her hands at the front of her shawl collar. She holds flowers in her hands with the stems extending below. Her hair is in short curls and she wears a bonnet with a yellow brim, decorated with a pink ribbon that matches her dress.

2in (5cm)	No. 6071	$75
3in (8cm)	No. 6070	$85
4in (10cm)	No. 6069	$95

This half-doll wears a bonnet that is similar to the one on the LEFT. Her hair falls below the bonnet and she wears a dress with a laced vest style in the front and puff sleeves. Her arms, bent at the elbow, return to her waist.

2in (5cm)	No. 5717	$70
2½in (6cm)	No. 5716	$75
3in (8cm)	No. 5715	$95

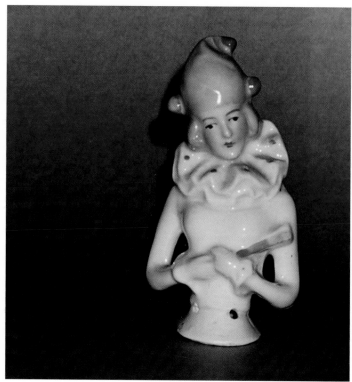

Dressed in her camisole, this model, with her head tilted to the side, wears a band of beads in her hair. One arm is tilted upward with the hand resting above her breast while the other hand rests diagonally at her right waist.

2½in (6cm)	No. 5669	$75
3¾in (10cm)	No. 5668	$90

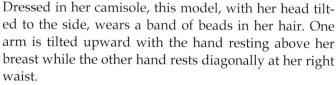

3¾in (12cm)	No. 5711	$130

A dark-haired flapper with her head tilted to the right, tucks her hands under her chin She has finely painted features.

2¼in (6cm)	No. 5890	$105
2¾in (7cm)	No. 5889	$125
3¾in (10cm)	No. 5888	$145

A model, with her hat at a rakish angle on her head, has a finely detailed bodice. Her right hand holds the brim of her hat, while the left hand holds a flower.

2¼in (6cm)	No. 5592	$125
2¾in (7cm)	No. 5591	$135
3¾in (10cm)	No. 5753	$155
4in (10cm)	No. 5590	$170

4¼in (11cm)	No. 5667	$120

This Pierrette wears her large ruffled collar and pointed clown's cap. Her detail, clothing and facial features are well defined. Her arms are bent at the elbows and returning to the front of her waist.

2½in (6cm)	No. 5713	$115
3in (8cm)	No. 5712	$125

A model lacking the detail of the previously mentioned model has her head tilted to the right, with her cheek resting on her hands. She wears a bracelet.

2¼in (6cm)	No. 5887	$85
3¼in (8cm)	No. 5886	$95
3¾in (10cm)	No. 5885	$105

A nude half-doll has shoulder-length ringlets and her hands reach behind her head.

2½in (6cm)	No. 5595	$105
3½in (9cm)	No. 5594	$115
3¾in (10cm)	No. 5593	$125

Simple Two-Piece Molds

A half-doll holding a large fan in her right hand with her head tilting away from the fan, appears to be flirting.

- 2½in (6cm) No. 6074 $105
- 2¾in (7cm) No. 6073 $115
- 3½in (9cm) No. 6072 $125

TOP RIGHT: This popular model is wearing a camisole, has her head tilting to the right and resting on her right hand with her left hand touching her right wrist. In her hair, she wears a wreath of flowers.

- 2in (5cm) No. 6089 $70
- 2½in (6cm) No. 6088 $80
- 2¾in (7cm) No. 6087 1/2 $95
- 3¾in (10cm) No. 6086 $125

MIDDLE RIGHT: This model wears a dress with large red-orange buttons that match her dangling earrings. Both hands touch the top of her bodice. She was sculpted as a flapper with her black hair in a bob cut.

- 2in (5cm) No. 5857 $60
- 2½in (6cm) No. 5858 $80
- 3¾in (10cm) No. 5857 $115

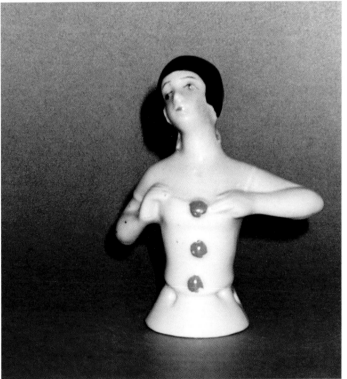

LEFT: This young woman holds her large brimmed hat at the brim where the ribbons would be attached. The ribbons are long, ending in a bow just above her waist. She has been found in a variety of pastel colors, such as lavender, light green and blue.

- 2¾in (7cm) Nos. 5796, 1936 $75
- 3in (8cm) No. 5795 $85
- 4in (10cm) Nos. 5794, 6293 $97

TOP LEFT: This little Dutch child holds red cherries by their stems and is very appealing.

▪ 2¾in (7cm)	No. 5725	$115
▪ 3in (8cm)	No. 5724	$120
▪ 3½in (9cm)	No. 5723	$135

MIDDLE LEFT: This child holds a fan. She wears a hair band in her blonde hair and her head is tilted to the side.

▪ 2¼in (6cm)	No. 5798	$95
▪ 2¾in (7cm)	No. 5797	$105

BELOW: This model is the same as the wigged model shown on the **BOTTOM LEFT**, except that this model has sculpted hair.

▪ 2¼in (6cm)	No. 5562	$70
▪ 2½in (6cm)	No. 5561	$75
▪ 3in (8cm)	No. 5559	$80
▪ 4in (10cm)	No. 5558	$85

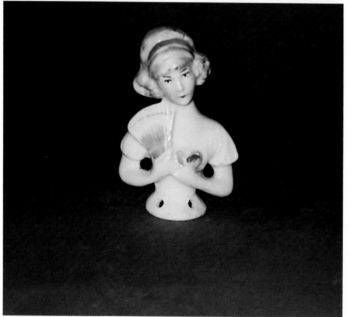

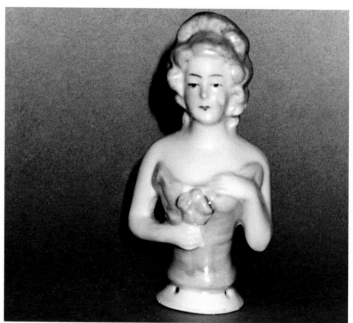

Wigged

BOTTOM LEFT: The wig on this model, although original, is sparse and messy. Her head is slightly tilted to the right. Her right hand rests at her left breast while the right hand rests at waist level, just under the other. She wears a camisole.

▪ 2½in (6cm)	No. 5168	$70
▪ 3in (8cm)	No. 5167	$90

Other Known Manufacturers

Other manufactures were producing half-dolls, but this value guide does not contain enough examples for individual sections of each of the companies featured here. There are many half-dolls that do have mold numbers but have not been identified as belonging to any specific manufacturer. There are many unmarked half-dolls that remain unidentified. The examples discussed and shown here are designed to provide some indication of the value of these and similar models.

Ernst Bohne Sohne
(Ernst Bohne & Sons)

THE Ernst Bohne porcelain factory began to produce porcelain in Rudolstadt in 1850. From 1856 until 1920, the factory made decorative porcelain, tea and coffee sets and figurines. In the 1920s, this porcelain factory became a branch of the Gebrüder Heubach porcelain factory in Lichte. Heubach sold the factory to Albert Stahl, who owned it from 1937 until 1974. From 1990 on, the factory has used the name "Albert Stahl & Co., formerly Ernst Bohne Sohne." One of the marks for this company was an "N" under a five-pointed crown. The other marks were anchors with the letters of "E" and "B" or only an "E." The ornate flowers that adorn the bodices, as well as elaborate fanciful hats, distinguish the half-dolls produced by this company. The figures are sculpted with exceptional detail.

ABOVE: This young woman is holding a vase.
- 4¾in (12cm)
  No. 9200 $1000

FAR LEFT: This young woman is holding a pencil and a slate with writing on it. She is very rare.
- 5½in (14cm) $1500

NEAR LEFT: This figurine, with her Dresden roses held in her left hand, wears another rose on her shoulder.
- 4¾in (12cm) $1000

Photo courtesy of Dave & Deryn Gipp

69

Baehr & Proeschild

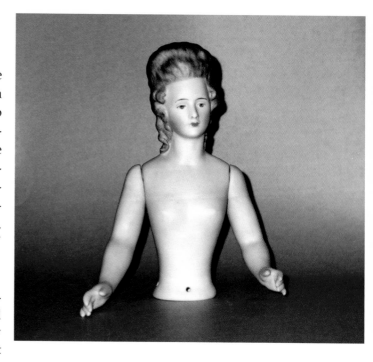

GEORG Baehr and August Proeschild founded the Baehr & Proeschild porcelain factory in Ohrdruf in 1871. In 1918, the Waltershausen doll maker Bruno Schmidt bought the Baehr & Proeschild factory. Before the purchase, Baehr & Proeschild made all the porcelain doll heads for the Bruno Schmidt doll factory using Schmidt molds. From 1919 on, the doll-related porcelain products of the joint doll and porcelain factory were marked with a trademark heart. Baehr & Proeschild included the initials "B" and "P" with their trademark heart.

TOP RIGHT: This model is bisque. Her molding is precise and the features are clear. Her arms are fastened with elastic to the shoulders. Her shoulder-length gray hair is molded into well-defined waves. She has a heart symbol at the small of her back and is nude. She has the number "3684" incised inside of each arm. Her fingers are molded very well. As a whole, this figurine is beautiful.

- 6½in (17cm)　　No. 3538a　　　$450

Conta & Boehme

THE Conta & Boehme half-doll children in the illustrations on the left appear to be those made by the porcelain factory of Gebrüder Heubach, the maker of the figurines of piano children. The faces of these half-dolls closely approximate those made by Gebrüder Heubach. However, the research of Marc and Shona Lorrin has uncovered information that verifies the maker as Conta & Boehme.

The little girl on the **FAR LEFT** wears her blue bonnet with roses on each side. Her curly blonde hair encircles her face and her little arms, separate from her body, beautifully illustrate the rounded little arms of a young child. The half-doll on the **NEAR LEFT**, holding a ball, has "googlie" eyes. The introduction of Rose O'Neill's Kewpies in 1913 prompted many porcelain factories to make dolls and half-dolls with side-glancing eyes. This little figurine has the wide-eyed look. The prices of either of these half-dolls would be similar.

- 2½in (6cm)　　$385

Fulper Pottery Co.

THE Fulper Pottery Co. in Flemington, New Jersey, produced bisque doll heads, all-bisque dolls and half-dolls from 1922 on. Many of their figurines and dolls lack the beautiful bisque and china appearance of German models. Yet these half-dolls remain important to collectors as the only ones produced in the United States during the early years of half-doll production.

TOP RIGHT: This model carries the Fulper Pottery Co. mark on the backside of the base. Her hands are attached to her body and she is nude. The painting on this figurine is well done, but the sculpting lacks the fine detailing of the European dolls.

- 6in (15cm) $135

Gebrüder Heubach

JOHANN Heinrich Leder's 1804 pottery factory in the German town of Lichte was the forerunner of the Gebrüder Heubach porcelain factory. Wilhelm Liebmann bought the Leder factory in 1830; and received permission from the ruling Duke to produce porcelain in 1832. Christoph and Phillip Heubach bought the porcelain factory in 1840. Phillip's son Louis was the sole owner in 1876. Louis' son converted the company into a shareholder company in 1904. In 1919, Ernst Bohne of Rudolstadt bought the porcelain factory. The name of the factory remained Gebrüder Heubach and the Ernst Bohne porcelain factory became a branch of the Heubach factory. In 1948, the factory became an East German government-owned company. The Gebrüder Heubach porcelain factory continues to make porcelain products today.

BOTTOM RIGHT: This half-doll is a product of the factory of Gebrüder Heubach. She is an exquisite model. Her hair is molded in waves and painted a light brown with individual hairs. Her head is tilted to the side and her expression is sweet. She has intaglio eyes skillfully painted and her arms are outstretched with her hands gracefully touching.

6½in (17cm)	No. 10424/2	$1500
7½in (19cm)	No. 10424/3	$2000
9in (23cm)	No. 10424/4	$3100

Photo courtesy of Gert Grollmuss

Herend

THE country of Hungary suffered through massive changes during World War II. It changed from a country ruled by royalty to a satellite country and was forced to practice the communist ideology.

Moritz Fischer founded the Herend pottery factory in Hungary in 1839. In 1939, the factory celebrated its centennial by designing a trademark that was used on the factory's porcelain products, including half-dolls. The company mark found on half-dolls contains the following words: "Centarium, Herend, 1839-1939."

TOP RIGHT & BOTTOM RIGHT: This half-doll model is molded in a national costume from Moravia. This was a village in Czechoslovakia, a neighbor of Hungary in Eastern Europe. Around her head she wears a beautiful white scarf with red embroidery which comes to a long point ending below her chest. She wears a white pleated blouse with sleeves that are full around her arms and carries the Herend mark, which provides clues to her age (1939).

- 7in (18cm)   No. 311 $1200

BELOW: This half-doll is a full-figure dressed in the native costume of Hungary. She is an exceptionally beautiful model and wears a red polka-dotted bandana around her hair. A short yellow vest with a laced front covers her blouse with its puffy sleeves. Her hands rest on her flowered skirt. The painting is delicate and flawless.

- 4½in (12cm)   No. 290 $850

Photo courtesy of Dave & Deryn Gipp

Photo courtesy of Dave & Deryn Gipp

Kestner & Co.

THE J.D. Kestner, Jr., doll factory was founded in Waltershausen in 1816. Jointed wooden dolls were the first doll-related products made during the early years. Kestner & Co. sold dolls with glazed porcelain heads from the 1840s on, although the factory did not buy the Steudinger, Müller & Co. porcelain factory in Ohrdruf until 1860. Following china head production, Kestner & Co. bisque doll heads mounted on composition bodies were popular with children. Doll collectors treasure the Kestner & Co. porcelain dolls in their collections, including the rare half-dolls. The half-dolls have sweet, expressive faces. They are molded in bisque rather than the more common china. Most of them have arms attached to the body with elastic strung through holes in the bodice. Their hands are very delicate. The half-dolls are very rare, but sought after by those who collect the all-bisques made by Kestner & Co., as well as by the half-doll collector.

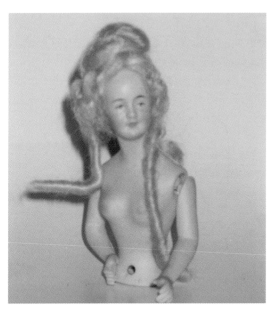

ABOVE: This beautiful little girl wears her Dutch hat with blue stripes. It almost covers the curls around her face. She also wears a white blouse with elbow-length sleeves. Over her blouse she wears a blue vest trimmed with black and "tied" with a black tie. She is a wonderful item.

- 3¼in (8cm)   No. 97v $355
- 4in (10cm)   No. 51B8 10 a $500

LEFT: This very rare half-doll is a beautiful example of the artistic workmanship of the Kestner Company. She is found in the J.D. Kestner Catalog "Teepuppen und Puderquastenkopfe…Tofel 24". The fine detail of her breasts is a characteristic of their half-dolls, as are her hands and facial expression. Her arms are joined to the body by elastic string that has lost some of the original elasticity. Her blonde mohair wig is in its original set.

- 4in (10cm)   No. 52B11a $600

Kämmer & Reinhardt/Simon & Halbig

THE Simon & Halbig porcelain factory was founded in Gräfenhain in 1869. The factory made bisque doll heads for many German doll factories. Following World War I in 1918, Carl Halbig was forced to sell the factory to the Bing Company in Nuremberg. This purchase joined the Simon & Halbig and Kämmer & Reinhardt factories. The Kämmer & Reinhardt doll factory, founded in 1885, became part of the Bing Werke (Works) in 1916. The production of half-dolls began in approximately 1927. They were illustrated in their catalog *My Darling Dolls*.

RIGHT: This half-doll is wax-over-porcelain, although the hands are bisque. The mark — "K*R" — is embedded on the back. She wears her original mohair wig styled as the waved bob of the flapper and she has a haughty expression. She does not have sew holes, but is attached to a cork inserted into the bust. The cork is covered with cotton and it is in this way she can be attached to a pincushion, tea cozy or lampshade. This model is not shown in *My Darling Dolls*, but is similar to the modeling of the bust of a Pierrot, and her arms and hands are identical to that model (Number 8/635).

- 5½in (14cm)   "K*R" $125

G.H. Macheleid,
Founder of the
Volkstedt-Rudolstadt Factory

G.H. Macheleid founded the company of Volkstedt-Rudolstadt in 1760 under the directives of Prince Johann Friedrich von Schwarzburg. It was the Prince who controlled the resources of the lands and forests of the region. Therefore, without his approval, manufacturing would have been impossible.

BELOW: This beautifully modeled half-doll wears a gold crown-comb in her brown hair. The individual waves and curls are evident due to the skillful modeling by the artist. This half-doll has outstretched arms with gracefully posed hands and is nude. The base is narrow. She carries the late mark (see Appendix A, PAGE 131) of the Volkstedt-Rudolstadt factory on the inside of her base. Another example can be seen in the bottom right illustration on PAGE 21, as she was sold through the company of Foulds & Freure.

- 5in (13cm) $500

MISSING TWO FINGERS:
- 5in (13cm) $175

Limbach

GOTTHELF Greiner founded the Limbach porcelain factory in 1772. It remained in business until 1939. The factory produced porcelain doll heads, all-bisque dolls and half-dolls. The mark of the Limbach Company is the cloverleaf.

This half-doll is a dramatic and stylized model of a woman. Her black hairdo includes a high topknot twisted to resemble a beehive. She wears a closely fitted black-trimmed dress. The blue bodice features a motif on the front. Her arms and hands are gracefully posed toward the front of her body.

- 6in (15cm)
  "[cloverleaf]"
  $600

Photo courtesy of
Gert & Gaby Grollmuss

Royal Rudolstadt

SEE "Netherlands" under the section on Sculpted Ethnic Costumes.

Unknown: Unmarked Half-Dolls

The half-dolls in this section are unidentified as to manufacturer and many do not even have a mold number. In some cases, the identification may be under clothing or a cushion that would result in damage if an attempt were made to find numbers or marks. The dolls are arranged according to how complicated the sculpting in the mold is and by how complete the figure appears to be.

French

THE half-dolls shown in the illustrations on this page were manufactured by an unknown French manufacturer. These half-dolls have characteristics that are different from their German counterparts. The porcelain is heavier, the arms are not as slender and they have a decidedly oval-shaped face. Both half-dolls have bases that taper much like the bases of the Dressel, Kister & Co. models.

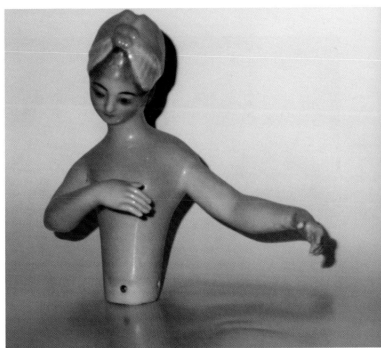

ABOVE: This nude model wears her hair in a turban. Her arms are held in a position that suggests a dance. Her features are well defined and skillfully painted.
- 4½in (12cm)   "France" $300

LEFT: This half-doll resembles the one shown **ABOVE**. She has gray hair that is swept toward the back of her head and holds her arms in a dancer's pose. She is marked "France" in red.
- 4¼in (11cm)   "France" $300

Children

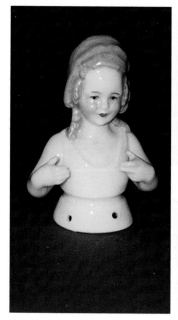
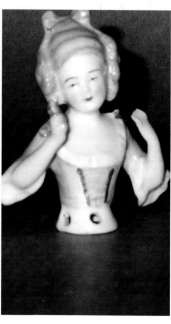

Arms Away

TOP, NEAR RIGHT: This child has long blonde ringlets and blue eyes. She wears a simple slip of white and both arms remain away from her body. The detail on this little half-doll is outstanding.
- 2¼in (6cm) $95

TOP, FAR RIGHT: This young teen is molded in Victorian dress. In one hand she holds her tube of lipstick and, in the other, her mirror.
- 2½in (6cm) $135

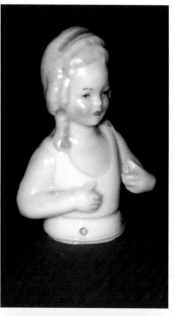

Arms Away and Returning

MIDDLE, FAR LEFT: This little girl is similar to the child on the **TOP, LEFT** and has her light brown hair styled in long ringlets as well. She wears a white slip rather than clothing. Her arms bend toward her bodice, but both of her hands touch the front of her bodice.
- 2in (5cm) $80

MIDDLE, NEAR LEFT: This sweet little Dutch child wears a traditional hat outlined in gold and holds fruit in her left arm which is molded close to the body. Her brown hair is molded as if it were under her hat with curly bangs showing. Her right hand rests against her chest with much of the arm separate. This particular model's clothing is in shades of pink and red. However, her dress has been painted in other colors.
- 3¼in (8cm) $65

BOTTOM LEFT: This child is very similar to the one shown **MIDDLE, NEAR LEFT.** She holds her basket of fruit in the right hand. The other hand appears to rest on the fruit but does remain separate from the rest of the figurine. This model is finished with skillful sculpting of a complicated mold and the painting is well done. Japanese manufacturers copied this model (see PAGE 46, illustration in the left-hand column, under "Holding Objects").
- 3½in (9cm) $135

Simple Two-Piece Mold

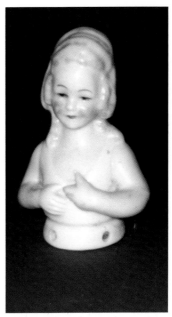

TOP, NEAR RIGHT: This child is very like the two children in the top left and middle left illustrations on the previous PAGE. She has blonde ringlets, a blue band in her hair and wears a white slip. Both of her arms are molded as a part of the front piece of the mold. The sculpting is sharp and the painting well done.

- 2in (5cm) $70

TOP, FAR RIGHT: This little child has "googlie" eyes and wears a big bow and a polka dot dress. Both of her arms are held against her front bodice. She looks very similar to the children manufactured by Conta & Boehme.

- 2¾in (7cm)   No. 22237 $185

Flappers

As a Complicated Mold

MIDDLE, LEFT: This beautiful nude flapper looks directly at the bird she holds in her left hand. Her facial expression suggests interest in her bird. Both arms are away from her body, her fingers are well defined and she wears her black hair in a "bob." The features are well defined both through the sculpting and the painting.

- 2½in (6cm) $195

Arms Away

BOTTOM, LEFT: This flapper wears her pink and blue cloche over her "bob" hairdo. Her blouse ends at her hips and is blue with a darker blue trim. One hand reaches toward her throat, the other arm bends with her hand toward the bodice. Her face has an expressive appearance.

- 3in (8cm) $180

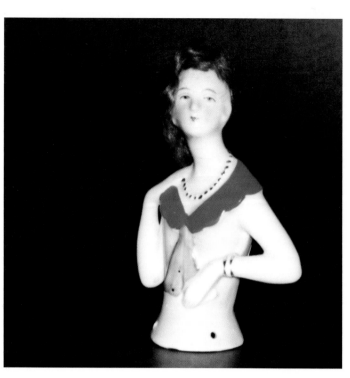

The head of this half-doll is tilted upward and she wears her original mohair wig. One hand, bending casually, touches her waist and the other hand touches the rose at her shoulder. She wears a pink top with a red inset and a bow at her hip where her blouse ends. The overall presentation is beautifully executed.

- 5in (13cm)   No. 3100 $305

This half-doll wears her original scruffy wig. Her yellow dress has an orange shawl collar that ends with a blue bow at the front .Her right hand touches her neck while her left hand touches her waist.

- 4in (10cm) $285

This nude lady with short hair holds a multicolored fan at the back of her head with her right hand. Her left hand rests at her hip. The painting of her facial features lacks skillful execution.

- 4¼in (11cm)   No. 5953 $260

Wearing a pink dress with the elongated waistline, this beautiful flapper also wears a pink hat that fits close to her head. Her blouse has a large white collar with a dark pink bow.

- 4½in (12cm)   No. -525* $250
  Number is illegible.

The arms of this flapper remain close to her body. She is wearing a pink dress trimmed in a darker pink color and a pink cloche. Because her eyes lack skillful detailing, she has a comical expression.

- 3¼in (8cm)   No. 7131 $125

At first glance, this figurine may look complicated because it was skillfully sculpted with a great amount of detail. Yet, the figurine is from a simple mold. This flapper wears a white hat trimmed with a ribbon and red and blue short dabs of paint. The dress has matching red and blue spots as decoration. She wears yellow gloves and holds her brown purse. The painting has been carefully done.

- 4in (10cm)   No. 6715 $225

Elizabethan Ladies

The women of the Elizabethan period wore large stiff collars with ruffs that stood up behind their heads. They had stiff-corseted low pointed bodices and the cuffs matched the stiff collars. Although the clothing suggests a romantic period in history, the head was actually held so stiffly that smiling became impossible.

This half-doll has powdered hair embellished with beads and wears a dark red dress. Her hands are away from her body. The detailing of this half-doll is exceptional.

- 3¾in (10cm)   No. 17558 $425

TOP LEFT: The collar of this half-doll required skillful molding. She has a bouffant hairdo and is dressed in green. She holds her hands at the front of her body. Her facial expression appears to be pained.

- 3¼in (8cm) $205

BOTTOM LEFT: This half-doll sits on its original cushion. The legs complete the figure. These features increase her value. The artist apparently lacked knowledge of fashion because this model wears a large stiff collar and a flapper bob. Her hands are lifted toward her collar.

- 2in (5cm) $215

BOTTOM RIGHT: This woman is ready for the masquerade ball and, with her mask and yellow skullcap, she would remain incognito. She sits on her pincushion and is complete with legs. Her collar of pink stands upright behind her head. She wears a white jacket over pink. Her price is increased because of her legs and cushion.

- 2¼in (6cm)   No. 416 $350

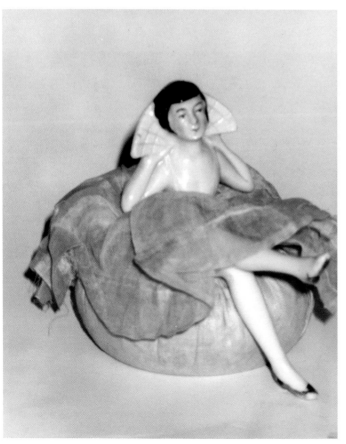

Elaborate and Complicated Molds

TOP LEFT: This woman has a Victorian hairdo with powdered hair. She is looking down at the basket of flowers in her hand. The flowers were applied after the mold was placed together and prior to firing. Her right arm bends slightly and extends downward away from her body. The other bends toward the front and holds the basket in such a way that the model appears to smell the flowers. The dress is that of the Victorian era, with a low neckline and ruffles at the end of the sleeves.

- 3¼in (8cm) $215

BELOW: This flapper half-doll wears nothing except her yellow hat which is decorated with red and blue flowers. Both arms are posed gracefully away from her body and are held in the manner of a dancer. Her fingers are finely detailed and her exquisite face has a dreamy expression.

- 3½in (9cm)   No. 5249 $215

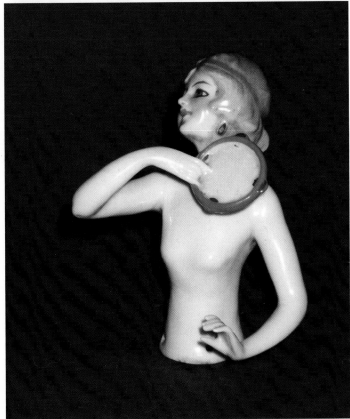

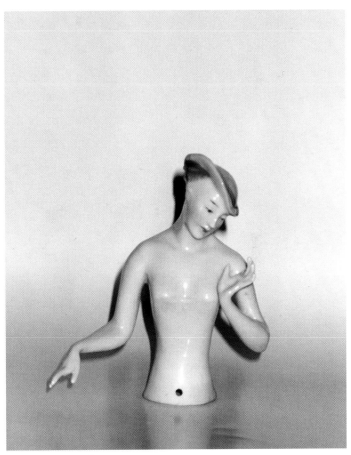

BOTTOM LEFT: This beautiful model of a flapper has her head turned to the right, with her chin tilted upward. Her eyes are outlined in the manner of the 1920s. Her right hand holds a tambourine to her shoulder while her left arm is held gracefully at her waist. Her fingers are beautifully sculpted.

- 3¾in (10cm) $425

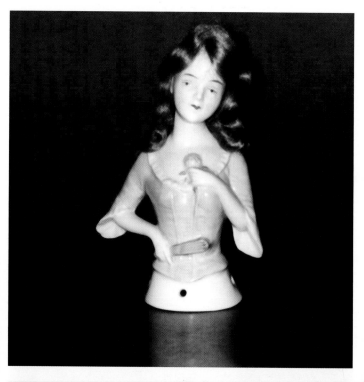

TOP RIGHT: This half-doll has one arm holding a rose (molded, not applied) just below her neck. The other arm bends at the elbow and she holds her fan in her hand. She is dressed in a Victorian style, with a pink dress that has a low-cut neckline. Her original mohair wig has waves falling past her shoulder.

- 4in (10cm)   "Sp1120" $235

This young woman has powdered hair adorned with a bow. She holds a flower to her chest and is wearing a blue dress trimmed with white ruffles. She is well painted and very appealing.

- 3½in (9cm)   No. 14165 $195

This model is found often. She wears a Victorian dress with an insert and her hair is decorated with flowers. She holds her hands as though she is praying.

2½in (6cm)	No. 6237	$50
3½in (9cm)	No. 765-*	$105
5¼in (13cm)	No. 7389	$225

Number is illegible.

A wide green fan adorns the light brown curls that fall to the shoulders of this woman. Her clothing is pink with a red insert. Her arms cross at her chest and in her hand she holds a fan.

- 2½in (6cm)   No. 4433 $145

Simple

This Victorian woman wears a pink bonnet. Unlike the half-dolls that have Dresden flowers, the flowers she holds were a part of the mold. She wears a white dress with a pink shawl wrapped around and her arms are against her body. The facial painting is well done.

- 1½in (4cm) $40

Others

Arms Away and Returning

This half-doll is small. One of her arms bends so that her hand touches her waist. The other hand is molded as part of the bodice and touches the necklace about her neck. She wears a blue dress and a corsage on her shoulder. The detail on this half-doll is poor.

- 1¾in (5cm) $50

PART TWO

Models with a Specific Feature

Brooms, Dusters and Shaving Brushes

One of the many uses of half-dolls included putting bristles on the base. The result was a broom, duster or shaving brush. These objects created a whimsical object and increased the number of potential buyers. The use of broom half-dolls did not occur until around 1920 and lasted until the 1930s. The brooms were used to sweep crumbs from the table, lint from a jacket or dress, and, in rare cases, provided a device for the application of lather to the face when shaving. During that time, Japanese companies copied many models of these half-dolls. Some of the broom dolls are marked "Made In Japan" on their backs. However, not all Japanese dolls are marked in visible areas so determining the origin of a doll can be difficult. Points that help determine the manufacturer include the quality of the painting and the features of the mold.

The base of the half-dolls holding the bristles varied. Some of the brushes were attached by gluing the bristles to the inside of the half-doll and hiding the sew holes with ribbon. However, it is evident that some of the dolls have no sew holes, but rather an ornamental base indicating that they were made to be used as a handle only.

The bristles of the half-doll brooms are finer than those of a household broom. They were dyed to coordinate with the colors of the half-doll. The figures are generally common half-dolls, although some full-figure dolls were used as well as animals and birds. The price is reflected according to the country of origin, the uniqueness of the figure used, how much wear is evident and whether the object retains its original box.

German Full-Figure Brooms

This full-figure flapper is wearing her lounging pajamas. Her condition is excellent and the bristles are in good condition. She was made in Germany. Her base has no sew holes.

- 8in (20cm)
  No. 9093 $95

This full-figure has a poorly painted face and wears lounging pajamas. Because of the painting on her face, she would be considered less desirable even though she is German made.

- 8in (20cm)
  No. 9092 $65

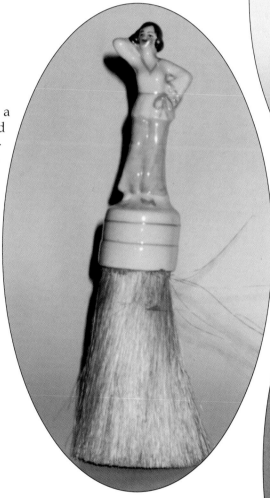

This full-figure is labeled "Gretel." In this instance, she was molded in a metal, but was made in porcelain as well. She had a mate named "Hans," and would have been one-half of a set. Her bristles retain their shape and color. The metal figure holds less value than the porcelain.

- 8in (20cm) $85

IN PORCELAIN:
- 8in (20cm) $115

German Half-Dolls

Additions of animals, dolls or other objects increase the value. This half-doll holds a broom. She is German, made by Hertwig & Co. There is slight wearing of paint, but the bristles of the broom remain in very good condition.

- 8½in (22cm) No. 8709 $145

This German miss is beautifully made. She holds her fan in her right hand while her left armed is posed gracefully and her head is tilted flirtatiously. The bristles retain their shape and color. Her ribbons are still beautifully shaped.

- 8in (20cm) No. 6903 $125

The German manufacturer Hertwig & Co. made this model. She is readily found as a half-doll and wears a small close-fitting bonnet over her long curls. The clothing and fan suggest that she is Victorian. Her features are well defined and she retains the original ribbon and lace about her waist. She is in unused condition. Rather than the bristles being rounded, they are flattened in the manner of a whiskbroom.

- 8½in (22cm) No. 8050 $125

This model represents the French Revolution period. Her dainty features are carefully painted. She wears a powdered wig, has a low neckline and carries a bouquet of flowers. While the doll is in excellent condition, the broom shows wear, as does the bow around her waist.

- 7½in (19cm) $85

This doll with the blue bodice represents the flapper era. The facial painting is finely done and she wears a rose at her shoulder. Her ribbons at her waist retain the original shape, as do the bristles of her brush. She is a common mold and one copied frequently by the Japanese.

- 7¼in (19cm) $70

This half-doll, although German, is of very poor quality. The color of her cheeks appears to be sprayed with a red paint that was carelessly sprayed on her neck and shoulders as well. The ribbon that should be around her waist is missing. The bristles on the brush are twisted although the color is retained.

- 7½in (19cm) No. 1726 $45

This half-doll was made as a handle as it does not have sew holes in the base. The broom is glued to the handle. The detail on this figure is well defined and the broom is in very good condition. This type of base produces a neat appearance but is more rare than brooms with sew holes and that difference increases the value. The Carl Schneider firm made this figure.

- 7in (18cm) No. --- 75* $110

*Numbers are illegible.

Hertwig & Co. made this half-doll. She is a Victorian woman and common. The ribbon has slipped below the sew holes and is quite soiled. The bristles are straight and do not look worn.

- 7½in (19cm) No. 8039 $45

Japanese Half-Doll Models

This little Dutch half-doll broom is in excellent condition. Her facial details are well defined and she wears her Dutch bonnet trimmed in gold. Her shawl collar and bouquet of flowers are also outlined in gold and her ribbons do not have evidence of wear. The bristles of her brush are multicolored in pastels. She is not common. While she is Japanese, these qualities influence her value positively.

   ▪ 8¼in (21cm) $95+

This model wears a top hat similar to that worn by men. While the detail of her features is crisp, the painting is not well done and she was made from a simple mold. Her ribbon does not show wear nor do the bristles of her broom. She retains her original box and is stamped on her back "Made in Japan."

   ▪ 8¼in (21cm) $95

This little clown was copied from a mold designed by the German manufacturer Gebrüder Heubach. Her painting is fair and the mold lacks the detail of the original. She retains her ribbon although it is soiled. The bristles of her brush are slightly faded and twisted.

   ▪ 7½in (19cm) $85

This little lady holding her hat with both hands is smaller than the previously mentioned examples. She is a copy of mold No. 5795 from Weiss, Kühnert & Co. She is slightly soiled with "Made in Japan" embossed on her back with a Morimuri emblem.

   ▪ 5½in (14cm) $85

Dogs and Bird

This little German shepherd appears to be placed on a man's shaving brush. It may have once had a shaving mug that came with it. The use of a half-doll as a shaving brush is unusual. The entire ensemble is in very good condition.

- 6¼in (16cm)
  No. 8577
  $115

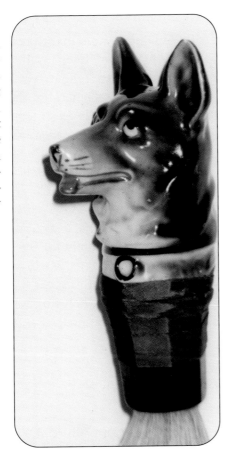

This little terrier with big ears is German. He has short bristles, lacks sew holes and was intended to be a handle. He could have been a shaving brush similar to the one shown on the left. He does not have a shaving cup but is very charming and in excellent condition.

- 5¾in (15cm)
  No. 8576
  $135

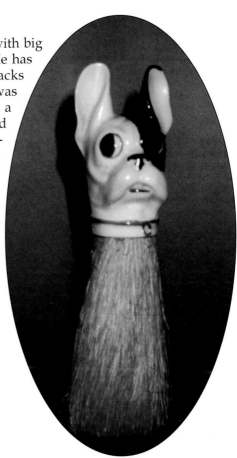

This Japanese terrier looks rather gloomy and is comical. His detail is crisp and the painting of his features is very good. The ribbon at his collar is soiled. His bristles have soiling at the edge but are, otherwise, in good condition. He is marked "Made in Japan" on his back.

- 8in (20cm)
  $85

This rather stern parrot is a German model. Aside from a little soiling, his condition is very good. His detail is crisp and the painting is carefully executed. He is a rare and interesting object.

- 7¼in (19cm)
  No. 9088
  $135

Chocolate Ladies

To have a Chocolate Lady is the epitome of a half-doll collection. The Chocolate Lady half-doll originated from a portrait by a Swiss artist, Jean Etienne Liotard. The Walter Baker Company was so enchanted by the portrait that it was copied on the company's Baker's Chocolate Tin (see Appendix B, page 132). The lady wears a close-fitting cap with a forward white ruffle. A little bit of hair shows at her forehead. Her bodice is gold with a white shawl collar and over her blue skirt she wears an apron.

On half-doll models, the colors on the clothing may be different from the original portrait. Her bonnet is a close-fitting cap or a Dutch hat and hairstyles differ as well. She carries a tray which can hold a pitcher, glasses or other objects related to serving chocolate or another beverage. On half-doll models, it is interesting to note that the trays and the objects on the tray may differ even on the same size model. This would indicate that the tray and its parts were all applied separately. Generally, the detail on these half-dolls was beautifully executed.

Several different companies manufactured these half dolls including Conta & Boehme; Dressel, Kister & Co.; Galluba & Hofmann; F. & W. Goebel; Carl Schneider; Sitzendorfer Porzellanfabrik; and other unidentified companies. Although the companies mentioned each have a section, the Chocolate Ladies are featured separately for the convenience of collectors. Each company is listed with the half-dolls they produced. The first number is the size, the second is the marking on the half-doll followed by the marking on the tray (if either exists) and the third is the value.

Conta & Boehme

The detail on this young woman is exquisite, even to the outlining of individual strands of hair. Her bodice does not have a shawl collar and is different from those of other half-dolls. She carries her tray with a chocolate pitcher and a cup.

- 3½in (9cm) $1200
- 4½in (12cm) $1400

Photo courtesy of Gert & Gaby Grollmuss

Galluba & Hofmann

THE half-dolls of Galluba & Hofmann often have no markings, making identification difficult. They are identified through characteristics such as a wide base and narrow waist. The underside of the base is glazed and often appears as though the body above the waist is solid. The facial features are delicate. The arms of the half-dolls are slender and the hands have beautifully sculpted fingers. It is difficult to distinguish the Galluba & Hofmann half-dolls from the models of F. & W. Goebel.

The selections shown here have close-fitting caps with the hair showing and molded in ringlets. The shawl collar ends in a tie. The half-dolls were made using one of two painting methods. With one method, the bodice would be colorful or white with hand-painted flowers on the bodice. The other method of painting used blue under-glazing of this color and is called delft. The colorful half-dolls shown here are listed first and the delft next. The value of the more colorful dolls is higher than the delft.

These half-dolls wear the Dutch bonnet, or "bulletie." The painted flowers on the clothing are absent.

- 4½in (12cm)   No. 9191 $1050 — $1500   LEFT
- 5½in (14cm)   No. 9190 $1200 — $1600   RIGHT

These half-dolls wear caps and the colorful costumes have decals.

- 4¾in (12cm)   No. 9191 $1000   LEFT
- 4¾in (12cm)   No. 9191 $1300   MIDDLE
- 5½in (14cm)   No. 9190 $1600   RIGHT

Photo courtesy of Dave & Deryn Gipp

This half-doll child carries only her pot. She has an angelic appearance with delicate facial features. Her clothing has gold trim and is beautifully detailed. She is very rare.

- 4½in (12cm)   No. 9398 $900
- 6in (15cm)   No. 9397 $1200

F. & W. Goebel

THE F. & W. Goebel half-dolls can be identified by a base that is very wide and larger than the bases of other manufacturers with the exception of those by Galluba & Hofmann. Most F. & W. Goebel half-dolls have the F. & W. Goebel mark on the back of their bases. (See Appendix A, page 131.) The style of clothing is from the Zeeland region of Holland. They wear close-fitting caps and their shawl collars end in a straight line under their chests. The bases of the half-dolls generally carry markings different from that of the tray. In each of the sizes of the half-dolls, the decoration of the cups and pots differ.

This delightful little child wears the winged Dutch bulletie which has beautiful detailing. She carries a coffee pot, creamer and sugar bowl outlined in gold. She is beautifully modeled. Her features are fine and very child-like.

- 5¼in (13cm)   No. 3867 $1500

Photo courtesy of Gert & Gaby Grollmuss

A

B

C

D

These half-dolls all have exquisite features. The flower decals on their bodices were applied prior to firing. Note that the chocolate pots differ in design according to the size of the doll.

3¾in (10cm)	"WG"	"4 9954"	$1100	A
4½in (12cm)	"WG"	"BT 181"	$1300	B
5in (13cm)	"WG"	"4 1/2"	$1500	C
6in (15cm)	"WG"	"5 1/2"	$2500	D

(possibly the only existing model in this size)

Unlike the previously shown models, these blue delft half-dolls — in two sizes — have the same design on the pot and cup regardless of their size.

4½in (12cm)	"WG"	"181 3 1/2"	$1150
5in (13cm)	"WG"	"181 4 1/2"	$1300

LEFT: This half-doll, named *Jeanette*, is carrying a coffee pot rather than the usual chocolate pitcher. She is often grouped within the Chocolate Lady category. Her cap is much different than the cap on the ladies featured previously. The decor on the bodice of this mold might differ from the half-doll shown here. She presents a wonderful variety for chocolate doll collectors.

- 4½in (12cm) "WG" $1100
- 5¾in (15cm) "WG" $1800
  "25 4 1/2"
- 6in (15cm) $2200

RIGHT: This half-doll is a young girl, possibly having her first tea party.

- 4¼in (11cm) "WG" $900+
  "8/1"

Photo courtesy of Dave & Deryn Gipp

Photo courtesy of Dave & Deryn Gipp

A.W. Fr. Kister

This model most closely resembles the portrait by Jean Etienne Liotard.

- 4½in (12cm) D326 "3" $2200
- 4¾in (12cm) $2500

Photo courtesy of Dave & Deryn Gipp

Carl Schneider

This child holds only a cup and her cap is very different than the caps found on other models. She has a sweet facial expression and is well sculpted. Her china is heavier than many models. Like many Carl Schneider models, she is marked "foreign" inside her base.

- 4½in (12cm) No. 13853 $700

Sitzendorfer Porzellanfabrik

TOP RIGHT: This model resembles the Jean Etienne Liotard portrait except for the beautifully painted detail on her shawl collar.

- 5½in (14cm) $2000
- 5¾in (15cm) $2200

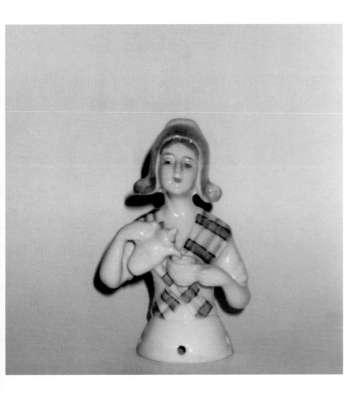

Unknown Manufacturers

ABOVE: This model is a child pouring her "chocolate" into a cup held in her left hand. She does not have a tray and lacks the fine detail of the other half-dolls, so is priced accordingly. Her clothing is blue and white.

- 3½in (9cm)   No. 4409 $560

BOTTOM RIGHT: This model is very similar to the Schneider model but bears no markings. She wears a Dutch bonnet that allows much of her hair to show. On her tray she carries a cup and a glass.

- 3¾in (10cm) $800

Dresser Figurals

A figural is a two- or three-piece figurine. The bisque and china figurals were designed to hold powder, rouge or other items used in the process of dressing. The top portion might be a half of a figurine while the bottom portion creates the skirt or the rest of the figurine. Other dresser figurals have full-figures that are on the top. Shown here are powder dishes, trinket boxes and ink bottles

These objects were designed to sit atop a lady's dresser. There are figures used primarily for powder. However, hairpins and other accouterments could be placed therein. Smaller containers might hold thread, needles, straight pins, safety pins, rings, cotton balls and a variety of other objects. Figurals were also made as ink bottle containers. Obviously, while powder could be expected upon a lady's dresser, ink containers would have been conveniently placed there as well. A lady might have used her dresser as a place to write letters or in her journal or to otherwise make use of a convenient ink dish.

The small sampling provided here may be used by the collector for comparison in pricing similar items.

Powder Jars

THE powder jars shown here will give width followed by the height of the total jar. If the jar has a mold number it will be printed next, followed by the value.

This powder box is an exquisitely detailed antique box made of hand-painted milk glass (opaline). The glass box is on a bronze stand. On the lid are pictures of a European couple. Pictures adorn the front and side of the jar as well. Inside rests a half-doll powder puff. The jar is beautifully gilded. A very rare and beautiful powder box, it has never been restored nor has the painting ever been touched up.

- 4½in x 4½in (12cm x 12cm) $650

ABOVE: Any art deco item designed by an artist called Robj is considered valuable and this powder box is no exception. The Oriental woman has her hair in a bun on top of her head. Her arms are sculpted away from her body while her face is highly stylized and is typical of the artist's work. The Liane Company in France made her.

- 7½in x 2¾in (19cm x 7cm)   No. 351 $560

ABOVE: This Victorian lady holds her skirt and looks down toward her little dog. She has lovely facial features, skillfully painted. She was made around 1900 and is marked "Germany." She is in excellent condition. The dog increases the value of this object.

- 3⅛in x 5¼ in (8cm x 13cm)   No. 3497 $265

BOTTOM LEFT: The Limoges Company of France made this young girl holding her mirror. The mark suggests that she was made in 1960. The painting and modeling are very sharp and her condition is very good.

- 5½in x 6in (14cm x 15cm) $89

BOTTOM RIGHT: This large round powder dish with Pierrot's head on the top was designed to have the bowl represent his ruffle. He has a soulful but attractive appearance. The date of manufacture is unknown but he is marked "Paris" on his underside.

- 5in x 4in (13cm x10cm) $175

TOP LEFT: This model is painted with a translucent paint. She was made from a simple two-piece mold for the top as well as for the bottom. Her arms are held next to her body. She is well painted and in good condition but gives no clue as to where she was manufactured.

- 4¼in x 5in (12cm x 13cm) $60

TOP RIGHT: This Victorian woman, sitting at her dresser and viewing herself in her mirror, is a great figurine. She has floral decals about her clothing that produce a delicate appearance. The mirror reflects her face. The top of the dresser can be lifted off to open the powder dish. This piece is marked "Made in Japan" but because it is skillfully made and in very good condition, it is a figurine with value.

- 6½ in x 6½ in (17cm x 17cm) $160

MIDDLE RIGHT: This Oriental figurine is very unusual. She has little wear but her painting lacks the skill or caring execution of the previously shown models. Because she is an Oriental, she can be expected to bring slightly more than a model of a young white female of similar quality. She is marked "Made In Japan."

- 3¾in x 5½in (10cm x 14cm) $85

BOTTOM RIGHT: This young girl, with her arms at her waist, is marked "Made in Japan." While her condition is very good, she is poorly painted.

- 3¾in x 5in (10cm x 13cm) $50

Trinket Boxes

The Hertwig & Co. factory made this beautiful container, but the mark on the bottom is very faint. The face of the child is beautiful and looks downward at the object she is holding.

- 3½in x 6¾in (12cm x 17cm) $285

This Pierrot, holding his lute, has a sweet expression. During the 1920s, Pierrots were popular figures. The gold on the outside of the jar and toward the back has worn off. This depresses his price slightly. He is marked "Made in Germany."

- 4½in x 6¼in (12cm x 16cm) $160

This model is a Pierrette, the female who, unlike the Pierrot, wears a little clown hat. Her face is lovely and well painted. She sits on a square box that is large enough to hold powder but, because it is square, could be considered a trinket box. It is marked "Bavaria" on the underside.

- 4in x 5½in (10cm x 14cm) No. 3150 $175

This toddler, in his bed, can be considered a desirable container. On the sides of his bed, paint has worn off. Otherwise, he is in very good condition. He was made in Germany and carries an unidentified mark.

- 3½in x 4in (9cm x 10cm) No. 3575 $160

NEAR RIGHT: This little girl in her pink dress was made in Germany. Her mold was a simple two-piece mold for both the top and bottom. Her features are well detailed and she is in good condition.

- 2½in x 3½in (6cm x 9cm)

  No. 40 $135

FAR RIGHT: This figurine is dressed to go out. She wears her little hat and carries a purse. Her features are delicately molded and skillfully painted. She is marked "Erphila" and "Germany" on the underside of the jar.

- 2¼in x 6in (3cm x 15cm) $150

FAR LEFT: George and Martha Washington are familiar figures for items produced around 1930. This small container has several places where the paint has worn away. The jar's molding is crisp. It appears to be German but is unmarked.

- 3in x 4in (8cm x 10cm) $80

NEAR LEFT: This little girl, with the tutu skirt of glazed netting, was made in Japan. Her arms are molded as a separate unit from her body, increasing her value. She is in very good condition as even the ceramic lace of the tutu is intact. She was probably made in the later part of the 1940s when the process of glazing lace was popular.

- 3in x 3½in (8cm x 9cm) $75

Ink Bottles

This bottle is painted in the orange color of the 1920s. The "cook" holds a rolling pin and has "googlie" eyes, providing a slight increase in value when compared to the eyes of other dolls. She has "Carter's Ink" embossed on her back and is marked "Made in Germany" with a mark similar to that used by Gebrüder Heubach. She is charming and in very good condition.

- 2in x 3¾in (5cm x 10cm) $280

This figurine, another bottle designed to hold ink and painted in the orange color of the 1920s, is that of a woman with one arm at her waist and the other covered with the shawl. She wears an apron and her features are not as carefully painted as most German models. Marked "Made in Germany" and "Erphila," she is rare and difficult to find.

▪ 2¾in x 4½in (7cm x 12cm)   No. 6002 $175

Drip Catchers

Drip catchers or "tropfenfängers" are just what the name suggests. They were designed to sit atop a teakettle and catch drips from the spout. An elastic cord held a sponge at the front, the drip catcher in the middle and a hook in the end. The sponge was placed under the spout, the drip catcher sat on the lid and the hook was held in place by attaching the hook to the handle as seen in the illustration below.

Drip catchers are diminutive objects, rarely reaching 1¾in (5cm) in length. The base was most often rectangular and slightly curved. This would permit the drip catcher to fit over a curved surface. However, this is not always the case. The drip catcher in this illustration is circular.

The drip catcher is not a half-figure but is included in this value guide because it has the same basic sew holes in

the base that half-dolls have. Many of the porcelain companies that produced the half-dolls, made the drip catchers. The advent of the drip catcher arrived years after the half-doll first appeared on the market. After World War II, the drip catchers were produced in Western Germany rather than in the East. The little objects rarely represented people, but rather butterflies, birds and animals. Drip catchers are reasonably priced.

Much of the information about the companies that produced them was lost during the war and after, as many of the manufacturing companies were destroyed or vacated. The area of East Germany that had produced so much porcelain and bisque was closed to western travel for many years. Information is slowly becoming available because researchers are now allowed to travel there.

Human and Fantasy Figures

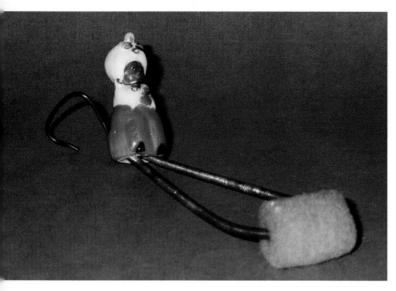

This little figure is a harem man. He is very desirable as he is rare. He still retains his hook and sponge. Rather than the elastic spring, the objects are held to the figure and the teapot by a very narrow spring.

- 1½in (4cm) $155

This little figure is a gnome. He wears clothing such as would be found on Santa's elf. He still has his hook and sponge and is charming and very rare.

- 1½in (4cm) $155

This diminutive woman wears a clown hat and is called a Pierrette. She does not have a sponge nor a hook so might be used as a puff handle as well as a drip catcher. She is found in several collections.

- 1½in 4cm) $45

Sitting next to the stork is his little baby. This figure is very appealing and difficult to find. This drip catcher has areas where the paint has rubbed off and, if this were a bird or butterfly, the price would be significantly reduced. Because of its charm, the price is only slightly affected.

- 1¾in (5cm) $155

This little boy sitting on his turtle is another whimsical and rare model. He is in excellent condition, his detail is crisp and the painting is well done.

- 1¾in (5cm) $165

Birds

BIRDS were frequently used as drip catchers. The birds represented many different species and often are beautifully detailed. Most have the rectangular base.

A: This drip catcher is a little parakeet. His head feathers are molded to a point. He is colorful but has lost his teapot accessories, thereby reducing his value.

- 1¼in (3cm) $60

B: This little blue bird has his elastic string at the front of his base. His hook and back string are missing.

- 1¼in (3cm) $45

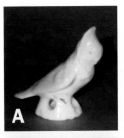
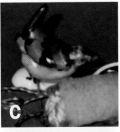

C: Hertwig & Co. manufactured this colorful little bird with his tail pointed upward. He still retains his elastic string, sponge and hook.

- 1½in (4cm) No. 4885 $85

D: This little bird is yellow and blue. He wears a label that states "Made in West Germany." His base is oval and curved and he lacks the elastic cord, sponge and hook.

- 1⅛in (3cm) $60

Butterflies

BUTTERFLIES were also used as drip catchers. It is easy to imagine how lovely they would be on top of a flowered teapot. The lid would stay put, too.

A: This smaller orange "butterfly" is actually a moth. Note the "eyes" on the wings that are designed by nature to appear as eyes to predators. The model for the moth is a Clouded Yellow. The Schmetterling Company of Germany produced this drip catcher around 1930. This moth is small and in excellent condition but, because it lacks its sponge and hook, its value is reduced.

- 1in (3cm) $40

B: This yellow butterfly is a form of a Yellow Swallowtail. It has the "tails" at the end of the bottom wings.

- 1¾in (5cm) $40

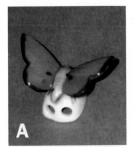
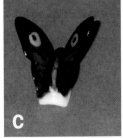
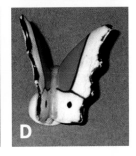

C: Hertwig & Co. manufactured this lovely drip catcher. It is a moth called a Peacock. It is very colorful and would provide interest to a drab teapot. It is in excellent condition but lacks the sponge ensemble.

- 1½in (4cm) $65

D: This butterfly is an unknown variety. The Schmetterling Company of Germany produced this drip catcher which is delicately painted and in excellent shape.

- 1¾in (5cm) $60

Animals

This drip catcher is a little red dog. He is very appealing and has great detailing despite the small size. He lacks the hook, elastic and sponge. The German Company of Seltener manufactured him in the 1930s.

- 1½in (4cm) $85

This pig lacks the sponge and hook and is difficult to find.

- 1½in (4cm) $60

Sculpted Ethnic Costumes

Several companies designed half-dolls that reflected various ethnic costumes. Dutch dress was very popular and almost every porcelain manufacturer has one or more examples of this mode. Other costumes were sculpted including Spanish, French, Egyptian, Czech Republic, Native American, Chinese, Japanese, Egyptian, Hungarian and German. Perhaps the manufacturer that created the most representative samples was the firm of Carl Schnei-der. The company's catalog contained a series of models called "Costumes of Foreign Lands" which are shown here. The catalog from F. & W. Goebel listed a series called "Volkstrachtren" or half-dolls in national costumes as part of that company's dolls in the historical series. Hertwig & Co. sculpted several varieties of Spanish women, many as dancers. A sampling of the half-dolls shown here have been chosen to exemplify these styles.

Oriental

RIGHT: This Oriental woman has her hair in plaits and her ears are decorated with oval coverings. The green bodice has a high neckline with an orange border fitting closely to her neck and the straight jacket has a double row of buttons. The sleeves fit tight against her arms. She holds her oval fan against her body with both arms molded away from her body and returning, with her hands at the front of her waist. The painting is well done. The maker is unknown, but such a mold is rather rare.

- 3½in (9cm)   "Nippon" $165

Czech Republic

LEFT: This young woman wears a costume of the Czech Republic consisting of a white blouse with short sleeves, over which she wears a laced vest of red. Her head is covered with a scarf tied at the side. She carries a sheaf of wheat in her left arm. Both arms remain close to her body and the hands are held toward her front. The mold is crisp and the painting is skillfully done.

- 3½in (9cm)   No. 76792 $215

Egypt

ABOVE: This exceptionally beautiful Moroccan dancer has her head decorated with a striped band that holds large green and orange puffs over her ears. Her upper body is nude and she is arched backwards. The right arm is held gracefully away from her body while her left arm is behind her skirt. Her toe is pointing out from her wide yellow skirt which has an unusual decoration outlined in gold. She wears a black sash trimmed with gold diamond shapes and is very graceful.

- 2¾in (7cm) $395

RIGHT: This Egyptian model is very different from the dancer **ABOVE**. She is sitting with her legs crossed and her hands resting on her knees. She wears a blue dress which covers her body and has a yellow and black decoration in front. The sleeves are narrow along her arms, but at the shoulders, there are little "wings" extending beyond her shoulders. She wears a yellow headpiece over a white cloth that covers her hair. She is extraordinary and carries the Sitzendorfer Porzellanfabrik mark.

- 3in (8cm)   No. 25027 $275

It seems that Egypt was a fascinating subject to the manufacturers of half-dolls. One popular subject was said to be Cleopatra. Several similar models have been found. Carl Schneider manufactured a model from the company's "Costumes of Foreign Lands." She wears a headpiece that appears to resemble a small crown and has bangs that are cut to a point at the middle of her forehead. Her straight, black hair falls to her shoulders and

she is nude. Her arms are away and up toward her breasts, with the hands bent at a right angle toward each other.

- 4in (10cm)   No. 14291 $315

RIGHT: This Egyptian prince is wearing a dark red headdress that covers his hair. The ends of the headdress fall to a point on each side of his head and are decorated with a yellow and black motif. He has one hand held against his body while the other is away with a finger pointing upward. The finger appears to be broken although the same mold owned by others has a similar "broken" finger. He has a bracelet on each upper arm. It may be that this is an unmarked Sitzendorfer Porzellanfabrik product, as the numbers match the sequence of that company.

- 2¾in (7cm)   No. 23451 $195
- 3in (8cm)   No. 23151 $205

France

RIGHT: This half-doll, produced by F. & W. Goebel, is very popular. She has a gold label marked "Nr. 31 / III, Elsasserin." She wears a huge ribbon depicting the costume of Geispolsheim in the Alsace region of France. The sleeves of her fringed shawl fall down three-quarters of the length of her arm. Over her blouse, she wears a corset laced in the front. One arm returns with the hand near her waist while the other hand rests at the middle of her shawl. She was made using two methods of painting — one using the colors of the Alsace region, while the other uses the blue under-glazing known as delft. She is skillfully sculpted and beautifully painted.

- 5½in (14cm)   "WG" $460

Germany

A half-doll wearing a costume from Schwalm, in the State of Hessen in southwestern Germany, has the top of her head covered by a small red cylinder called a Betzel and tied by a black ribbon. She wears a white blouse with a red border and her high collar is molded and painted to suggest embroidered flowers. Her arms bend at the elbows with her hands at her waist and in her right hand she holds flowers. She is well molded and expertly painted.

- 3in (8cm)   No. 19427 $300
- 3½in (9cm)   No. 19421 $325

Hungary

A model of a gypsy from Hungary wears a blue scarf over her black shoulder-length hair and very large, yellow hoop earrings. Her blouse, with a low neckline, is white and the front is draped. Over her blouse she wears a light green vest and over the green vest she wears a red vest. She has a large necklace that appears to match the earrings and she wears bracelets of yellow on her arms that are away from her body. She was manufactured by Carl Schneider for the "Costumes of Foreign Lands" series.

- 3¾in (10cm)   No. 14393 $450
- 4½in (12cm)   No. 14392 $525

TOP RIGHT: This young girl represents a gypsy. Her dress is less ornate than the gypsy model described previously. She wears a green scarf over blonde hair and her blouse is covered with a wide pink shawl. Both arms are molded against her body with one hand pointing toward her blue necklace. Her painting is delicate, as is the sculpting.

- 3in (8cm) $165

A model very similar to the model shown on the **TOP RIGHT**, but appearing older, wears a red scarf and a white shawl with a red border and black polka dots. The shawl covers her black blouse. Her arms are molded against her body and her painting is less skillfully done when compared with the painting on the model ion the **TOP RIGHT**. This model appears to be another one produced by the Carl Schneider factory.

- 3½in (9cm)   No. 14341 $165

MIDDLE RIGHT: This half-doll model is in a native costume. She has an oval-shaped head with her hair worn in a long braid falling to the middle of her back. Her blouse is red and black with a molded belt embellished

Head-dress photo courtesy of Gert Grollmuss

with green flowers. She wears a gilded "crown," with beads sewn on, which was not part of the mold but was added at the factory. She has the beginnings of her skirt molded at her waist and in the back the skirt has a bow. She was made around 1835.

- 7in (18cm)   "[Herend mark]"$2200

At the front of the half-doll on the **MIDDLE RIGHT** is a full-figure with the entire costume molded. In both of the figures, facial features are stylized and skillfully painted. This one lacks the added crown.

- 5¼in (13cm)   No. 5403 $325

Japan

TOP RIGHT: This Japanese woman has a skillfully painted, heavily powdered face. Her hair is molded in a traditional style, worn during the late nineteenth century. She wears an orange kimono that is painted with "embroidered" flowers of white and blue. The sleeves are wide and bordered in yellow, as is the border of the kimono. Her arms remain close to her body, with the right hand holding a light blue mirror trimmed with dark blue flowers. She is another rare model.

- 3¾in (10cm) $165

Native American

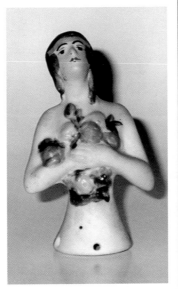

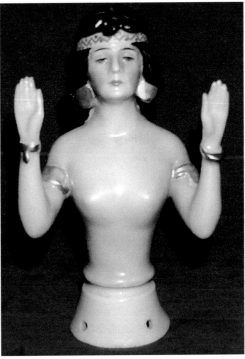

MIDDLE, NEAR RIGHT: This Native American is marked "France" on its base. She is molded from a simple two-piece mold and wears a headband. She is nude except for the flowers pressed close to her body through her arms. Her painting is amateurish.

- 3in (8cm)   No. 678 $85

MIDDLE, FAR RIGHT: This maiden is a superior model when compared to the one on the **NEAR RIGHT**. She has a decorated band around her head and wears large gold earrings as well as two gold bracelets on each upraised arm. Her facial detailing is beautiful. The manufacturer of this rare half-doll is unknown.

- 4¼in (11cm) $750

Photo courtesy of Dave & Deryn Gipp

Netherlands

MANY porcelain manufacturers sold models with a Dutch motif. Two models have been chosen to illustrate a Dutch half-doll. They are by Royal Rudolstadt and Carl Schneider. These are presented for purposes of comparison. Other models of Dutch costumes are shown throughout this book.

BOTTOM RIGHT: This model is an outstanding half-doll made by Royal Rudolstadt. Her clothing is painted in black and gold and her head is covered with her Dutch hat. She wears a simple blouse over her laced corset. The fingers of this half-doll are beautifully sculpted, as are the rest of her features.

- 3½in (9cm) $375

TOP RIGHT: This figure is that of a young woman holding a ball of yarn. She wears the winged Dutch hat and her light bodice is covered with a darker blue laced corset. She carries the Carl Schneider mark on her base. The arm holding the yarn is molded away from the body, while the other has her hand molded to the front of her bodice.

▪ 3in (8cm)	No. 5724	$120
▪ 3½in (9cm)	No. 5723	$135
▪ 4in (10cm)	No. 12529	$290
▪ 4½in (12cm)	No. 12527	$315

Spain

The "Flamenco Dancer of Andalusia," was sculpted for Hertwig & Co. (Andalusia is a mountainous district in Southern Spain.) Nude, she wears a comb in her black hair which is styled with a bun in the back. Her graceful hands hold castanets and extend upward.

▪ 4½in (12cm)	No. 6494	$495
▪ 5½in (14cm)	No. 6386	$595
▪ 6in (15cm)	No. 6443	$975

Another Spanish dancer, also nude, wears the authentic comb in her hair. Her fan is held in her right hand and touches her forehead. She lacks the exquisite molding of the Hertwig & Co. model. She was made by the Carl Schneider factory and carries the company's mark.

- ▪ 4½in (12cm)   No. 12527 $275

MIDDLE LEFT: This Spanish model wears her tall wide yellow comb in her black hair. She holds a yellow fan in her left hand and her left arm is raised and held as though waving. Both arms are held away from her body. Her red bodice is strapless, her molding is beautiful and she is skillfully painted.

- ▪ 3¾in (10cm) $275

Another model of a dancer wears her large comb in her black hair. Her eyes are emphasized with black lines. In her right hand, she holds a fan which touches her right shoulder. Her left hand is held behind her back (touching). Her bodice, with narrow shoulder straps, is draped close to her body and she wears a shawl that has hand-painted flowers.

- ▪ No. 8769 $85 – $125 depending on size

A model similar to the one previously mentioned and dressed the same, has her arms next to her body. Her right hand is at her breast and the other at her waist.

- ▪ No. 8779 $60 – $95 depending on size

MIDDLE RIGHT: The mantilla of this Spanish woman is pink and falls over her green bodice. She holds flowers in her left hand that ends at her waist while her right arm extends upward, away from her body with the hand returning to touch the veil. She is skillfully molded and painted.

- ▪ 2½in (6cm) $195

Another Spanish woman wears a yellow mantilla over her red bodice with her right arm pressed against her mantilla and her hand at her waist. Her mantilla is draped at the waist and appears to be embellished with grapes. Her left arm is away from her body with the fingertips of that hand held at her waist. The molding is sharp, but the painting is less skillfully executed.

- ▪ 2¾in (7cm)   No. 1005 $85

Full-Figures with Sew Holes

The manufacturers of half-dolls also made full figurines with sew holes. These items were used in much the same way as the half-dolls but did not require the finishing touch of clothing. They were placed atop pincushions, powder puffs, cushions and a variety of other items. They are more rare than the half-dolls but important to collectors who wish to have a sample of all related items. For brevity, similar items are illustrated together. This provides for comparison of size and finished details.

The figures have a design in common but then are identified in the value section by letters a, b, c and so on. The size of the figure is printed first, then the mold number, or mark, if known, followed by the value. After the value is the identifying letter that should help you locate the item in the illustration.

It seems that the majority of full-figure items were bathing beauties. Babies and children were very popular also.

Bathing Beauties

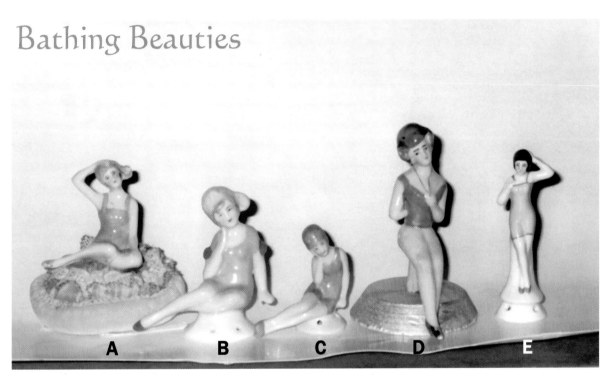

A: This bathing beauty in pink sits atop the powder puff that is original to her. She is used as a handle. Because of the powder puff, she has a higher value than if she were separate.

- 2½in x 2¼in (6cm x 6cm)   No. 7403 $160

B: This example wears a blue bathing suit, a bathing cap typically worn from 1930 to 1940 and red shoes. The base of this half-doll is very broad.

- 3¼in x 2in (8cm x 5cm) $145

C: This bathing beauty was molded with porcelain that had been tinted pink prior to firing. This technique decreases the value of the half-doll. She wears a blue suit which was painted on after the initial firing.

- 2in x 2in (5cm x 5cm) $115

D: This lady wears only a bodice. Although her legs are attached, it appears that she was intended to be placed on top of a pincushion and finished with a material covering. She was made with a simple two-piece mold and her painting is not well done.

- 3½in x 2¼in (9cm x 6cm) $125

E: This standing model might be used as the handle of a powder puff. However, her length would decrease the variety of objects on which she would be used.

- 3¼in (8cm)   No. 5722 $115

Nudes

LEFT: This bathing beauty can be placed on items belonging in the bedroom.
- 1¾in x 3½in (5cm x 9cm)
  No. 16218 $190

RIGHT: Dressel, Kister & Co. made this model. She is seated and could be placed on many items and has also been found on a wooden base. She is very expensive
- 3in x 3½in (8cm x 9cm)
  "[Dressel, Kister & Co. mark]" $460

Babies

BABIES are very desirable full-figures and are featured below.

A: This beautiful baby is very appealing with an angelic face. Even the tiny fingers are beautifully defined.
- 2¼in (6cm)   No. 6344 $285

B: This tiny baby is standing with widespread arms. She is sewn onto a powder puff. This is an original presentation and increases the value.
- 2¼in x ¾in (6cm x 2cm) $165

C: This delightful baby was made with pink-tinted clay. One arm is raised to wave and the other is at her side. The painting is well done but the base has been repaired.
- 2in (5cm) $80

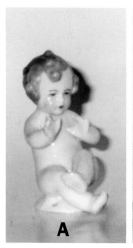
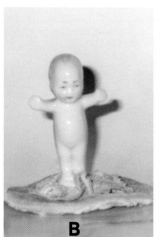

A   **B**   **C**

Children

THE two children shown on the right are rare.

A: This child is dressed to play in the rain. She is wearing a yellow cape and is missing her umbrella.
- 3¾in (10cm)   No. 6348 $130

B: This child is dressed as a clown or Pierrot. He wears his little red skullcap and white clown coat decorated with red puffs.
- 3in (8cm) $120

A   **B**

Flappers

FULL-FIGURES molded as flappers are shown below.

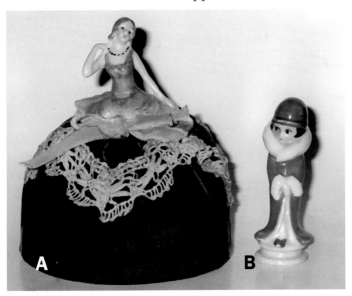

A: This little model sits on top of a pincushion. She is finely detailed, despite her diminutive size. She sits on her knees hidden under her purple dress and her hands are gracefully posed. Even the beads around her neck are skillfully painted.

- 2¼in (6cm) $130

B: The F. & W. Goebel factory manufactured this little flapper around 1950. She wears her full-length coat with its fur collar and a green cloche. She has "googlie" eyes and is a very appealing figurine.

- 3in (8cm) $145

Others

THESE two models could be headed for a dance.

A: This little model is a gentleman with a top hat. He is dressed in his little green suit and wears a blue polka dot tie. In both arms he holds bundles of roses. He is made from a simple two-piece mold and his features are well painted. If used on a pincushion, his hat is sized to hold a thimble.

- 3in (8cm)   No. 15140 $125

B: This model was sculpted after a painting of Mademoiselle Marie Ann de Cupis de Camargo by Nicolas Lancret. While very petite, the detail is excellent. She is a favorite of collectors, but not easily found. The factory of Carl Schneider made her.

- 2¾in (7cm)   No. 14843 $255

Half-Dolls with Bases

The 1920s were a time of frivolity. The "modern" woman had a feminine dresser containing wonderful articles to adorn her face and hair. The bob was a simple straight haircut, ending at the lobe of the ear. Gone were the long ringlets and the bouffant hair. Instead, the focus was the face. Eye makeup, rouge, lipstick and powder replaced hairpieces. With the emphasis on the face, the powder puff doll was born. The powder puff doll was of two pieces, both porcelain. The most common model was a Pierrot and Pierrette in a flirtatious pose. Other models were women in the angular pose of the art deco period and flappers. The upper figure was a half-doll with a powder puff attached. The puff might be entirely made of swan's-down, or a velveteen puff surrounded by swan's-down. The bottom portion held the powder and the puff. In the 1920s, the figures were sold separately or as a unit and could cost as little as $2.00 each.

Primary manufacturers of these units were the companies of Dressel, Kister & Co.; Hertwig & Co.; Carl Schneider; and Sitzendorfer Porzellanfabrik. Some of the bases are found marked "Paris, France." German manufacturers such as Dressel, Kister & Co., Hertwig & Co., Carl Schneider, or others might make the powder puff half-doll sitting on a powder base. To provide a concise identification, several similar items are featured together in one illustration.

The height is given first followed by the mark or model number, if known. The value is shown next and then the identifying letter that should help you locate the item in the illustration.

Full-Figure Standing

BELOW is a grouping of half-dolls which have been made into full-figures by sewing the half-doll onto a ball of cotton, cork or sawdust which is covered with fabric and then sewn onto a base. The half-dolls and the bases were sold separately. The figure could be dressed and used as a pincushion or decoration.

A: This redheaded model has both hands touching the back of her head. Her molding is crisp and the material joining the half-doll to her base appears original to this figurine. The firm of Sitzendorfer Porzellanfabrik made the base.

■ HALF-DOLL:	3½in (9cm)	
■ BASE:	3½in (9cm)	No. 8200
■ FIGURINE:	8½in (22cm)*	TOTAL VALUE: $500

B: This flapper is brushing her hair. Her identity is unknown but the base has the Sitzendorfer Porzellanfabrik mark.

■ HALF-DOLL:	2½in (6cm)	
■ BASE:	2in (5cm)	No. 5273
■ FIGURINE:	6in (15cm)*	TOTAL VALUE: $425

C: This flapper has black hair, heavy eye makeup and holds a mauve poppy. Her puff is trimmed with mauve swan's-down that matches the color of the grapes on the base. Carl Schneider made the base. The half-doll's marking is covered with fabric.

■ HALF-DOLL:	4¾in (12cm)	
■ BASE:	3¾in (10cm)	No. 15308
■ FIGURINE:	9¼in (24cm)*	TOTAL VALUE: $750

D: This figure is beautifully molded and her painting is well executed. The upper unit skin color matches the legs in the lower unit. Sitzendorfer Porzellanfabrik made both units. The entire piece is very appealing.

■ HALF-DOLL:	2½in (6cm)	No. 22687
■ BASE:	2in (5cm)	No. 5360
■ FIGURINE:	5¼in (13cm)*	TOTAL VALUE: $485

E: This lady was molded and painted in the angular art deco style. She lacks the exterior cloth that would cover the cotton. The half-doll and the base look appropriate together and are original to each other.

■ HALF-DOLL:	3in (8cm)	No. 5475
■ BASE:	3in (8cm)	
■ FIGURINE:	7in (18cm)*	TOTAL VALUE: $525

F: This beautiful flapper, with a rose behind her left ear, is delicate and well painted. Her base matches her clothing, although her costume is more recent than either part. Her marks are unknown.

■ HALF-DOLL:	4½in (12cm)	
■ BASE:	3½in (9cm)	
■ FIGURINE:	8½in (22cm)*	TOTAL VALUE: $750

*The total height of the unit is greater than the addition of the half-doll and base as a result of the fabric in the middle.

Pierrot and Pierrette Units

A B C

IN the delightful powder puff examples shown on the right, the size of the half-doll's upper body seems proportional to the bottom unit.

A: This Pierrot is on bended knee, offering his heart to Pierrette who is playing her mandolin to entertain him. The Pierrot has slight paint wear but this is insignificant to the value of the entire unit.

- **HALF-DOLL:** 3in (8cm)
- **BASE:** 4in x 5¼in (10cm x 13cm) No. 7476
- **FIGURINE:** 8½in (22cm) TOTAL VALUE: $1800

B: This larger Pierrette is playing her mandolin for Pierrot. He is bending his knee so that she can stand on it as she plays. Each unit complements the other in quality, detail and size. This is a beautiful and highly desirable figurine.

- **HALF-DOLL:** 5in No. 5096
- **BASE:** 7¼in x 5½in (19cm x 14cm) No. 6072
- **FIGURINE:** 13¾in (35cm) TOTAL VALUE: $2500

C: It seems that Pierrot is a romantic figure. This Pierrot allows Pierrette to stand on his chest as he supports her. These units seem very appropriate to each other in size and quality.

- **HALF-DOLL:** 3¼in (8cm)
- **BASE:** 3¾in x 4½in (10cm x 12cm) No. 10250
- **FIGURINE:** 8in (20cm) TOTAL VALUE: $1600

Müller & Co.

This half-doll has her bouffant hairdo embellished with flowers and a feather. She is all-original — her cushion is filled with straw, the powder puff is swan's-down and the silk is "melting," but the beauty of her elaborate clothing is evident. She is stamped on the backside of her base and was made around 1905.

- 5½in (14cm) No. 9435
- 4¾in (12cm) "[Müller & Co. mark]"
- 14¾in (38cm)* $2200

Total size with cushion.

Dressel, Kister & Co.

This little Victorian still has her delicate roses in her hair, while holding a rose in her right hand. The fingers of her hands, although tiny, are beautifully detailed. Her base fits the swan's-down puff which she retains, but the legs are a deeper color than her arms, so it is uncertain whether the base was original to the puff. In the 1920s, bases could be purchased separately and it appears that this was the case with this example. Although she is small, the quality of this half-doll is excellent.

- 3in (8cm)   "[Dressel, Kister & Co. mark]"
- 2½in (6cm)   base, marked "Made in France"
- 6¼in (16cm)   TOTAL VALUE: $800

Others

THE half-dolls shown below do not fit in the other groupings. Yet they are units that are beautifully made with the half-doll and the lower unit fitting together to present pleasing figurines.

A: This flapper holds her parrot on her left arm. The base suggests that she is sitting. She has a swan's-down puff that fits in the bowl of the bottom half. Her condition is excellent.

- **HALF-DOLL WITH PUFF:** 2⅞in (7cm)
- **BASE,** MARKED "REGISTERED DRGM":
  1in x 5in (3cm x 13cm)   No. 5856
- **FIGURINE:**   4in (10cm)
  TOTAL VALUE: $800

B: This figurine is a tall 12in (31cm) model by the factory of Carl Schneider. The face is excellently sculpted with beautifully detailed features. She has the index finger of her left hand extended toward her face. Her curls are molded, rather than only painted on and she is all-original.

- **HALF-DOLL WITH PUFF:**   7in (18cm)
                              No. 14260
- **BASE,** MARKED "REGISTERED DRGM":   5in (13cm)
                              No. 5541
- **FIGURINE:**   12in (31cm)   TOTAL VALUE: $1700

A   B   C

C: This flapper was made by Weiss, Kühnert & Co. and the base by Sitzendorfer Porzellanfabrik. The naughty Pierrot has his head under the skirts of the flapper. She appears unconcerned. Her swan's-down puff matches the paint representing the ruffles of the skirt that is a part of the lower unit.

- **HALF-DOLL:**   3½in (9cm)   No. 6102
- **BASE:**   4¼in (11cm)   No. 26022
- **FIGURINE:**   8in (20cm)   TOTAL VALUE: $1250

Heads

The manufacturers of half-dolls certainly were versatile. Among the items related to the half-dolls are the models which were just heads alone. The heads could be used in a number of ways. They could be found as corks which act as bottle caps or allow liquid to flow from a hole in the cork out of the head. They are found as a part of a handle, on powder puffs or napkin rings. Some do not reveal any clues as to their original purpose.

The size of the porcelain head is given, followed by the mold number or mark, if known. The value is shown next and then the identifying letter that should help you locate the item in the illustration.

Heads with Corks Attached

THE first three heads shown below (A, B, and C) have bases that are hollow. A cork fits into the base and is hollow also. The size given is for the porcelain and excludes the cork.

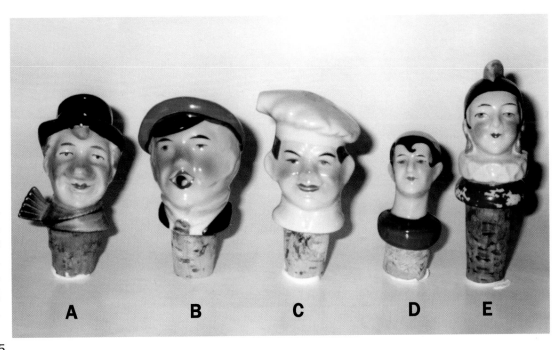

A   B   C   D   E

A: This man is a dandy. He wears a top hat and scarf and has a broad grin and red nose. He certainly has had enough to drink because, if tipped, liquid will pour from his nose.
- 2½in (6cm)
  No. 3635 $75

B: This gentleman wearing a red cap has a starched collar and a bit of his tie is evident. His painting is well done. The liquid flows from his mouth.
- 3¼in (8cm) $80

C: This little baker has a hole at the side of his hat. The liquid pours from the hole. The cork is fastened around the base of the head. He is marked "Germany" on the bottom of his base.
- 2½in (6cm) $80

D: This Pierrot or clown head model has a cork without a hole inside it. It was designed to top a bottle, but would need to be removed before liquid could be poured. He wears the traditional skullcap and "spit" curls and is marked "Germany."
- 2in (5cm)   No. 95 $40

E: This Pierrot with the feather in his skullcap has some paint flaking off. Under his chin he has a wide collar which covers a hole by fitting over the top of a bottle.
- 2½in (6cm)   No. 6331 $45

Pierrots with Narrow Bases

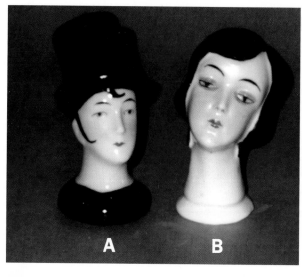

A: This model with the "spit curls" of the Pierrot wears a formal top hat rather than the skullcap. He could have had a cork within his base or have been used for a number of other things. His detailing is sharp, the painting is fine and his base is incised "Germany." He is in excellent condition.

- 2½in (6cm)   No. 6327 $105

B: The detail and painting on this Pierrot is excellent.

- 2in (5cm) $90

Pierrots with Ruffs and Sew Holes

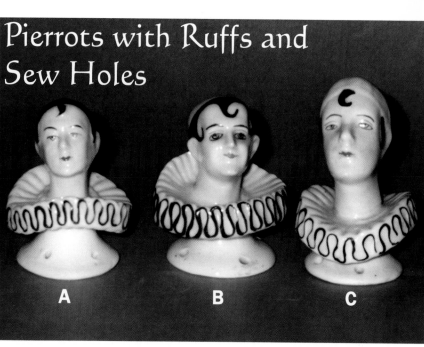

THE Pierrots on the left wear the traditional outfits with ruffled clown collars.

A: This Pierrot has a solid base with the exception of sew holes. His overall appearance is delicate and the sculpting is sharp.

- 2¼in (6cm)   No. 36 $125

B: Even though this Pierrot has a ruffled collar and the traditional appearance, the painting lacks the fine detail of the others seen here.

- 2¼in (6cm)   No. 7 $110

C: The collar of this Pierrot has crisp detail. His neck is elongated and he is exquisite in sculpting, painting and overall appearance.

- 2½in (6cm) $135

Pierrettes

GENERALLY, the male Pierrot wears a skullcap and the female Pierrette wears a pointed cap. The two models on the right are females.

A: This head, wearing the white clown hat with black hair showing below the brim, is marked "Germany." The painting of her facial features is excellent although lacking the appeal of example **B**.

- 2½in (6cm)   No. - - -91* $100
Numbers are illegible.

B: This happy model, wearing a jester's hat of yellow-green, has well defined facial details. She seems to know a jolly secret, as her eyes almost twinkle and her mouth is turned up in a smile. The painting is excellent. She has a matte finish and was manufactured by A.W. Fr. Kister.

- 2¾in (7cm) $135

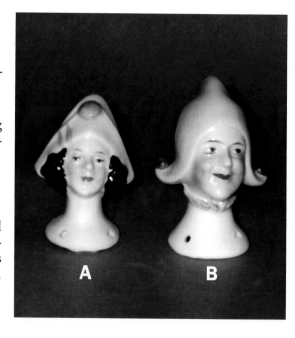

Children

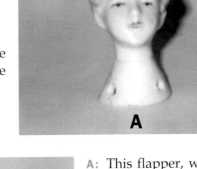

A: This little boy wearing a red cap is a sweet model. He is well painted and has eye appeal.

- 1½in (4cm) No. 4837 $95

B: Another little child wears a lavender hat over blonde curls, has a sweet expression. He was carefully made and remains in excellent condition.

- 1½in (4cm) No. - - -60* $95

Numbers are illegible.

Flappers

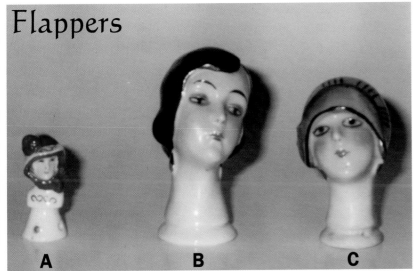

A: This flapper, wearing her bonnet with red trim and a red ribbon, is a petite model.

- 1¼in (3cm) No. 10/2 $60

B: This beautiful flapper with a long neck is graceful in appearance. Her detail and painting are excellent.

- 2½in (6cm) No. -011* $135

Number is illegible.

C: The lavender cloche worn by this flapper is carefully detailed. Her eyes are outlined in the manner of the 1920s and her mouth is painted in a smile with lovely lips and small teeth.

- 2¼in (6cm) $150

Stylized Heads

THE two heads shown here have certain characteristics of half-dolls with the same or a similar head.

A: This head is marked "France." She appears to be designed by the French artist Robj. Her face is an oval with the features suggested through the painting. The facial detail suggests an Oriental person, but this is the face often suggested by Robj's work.

- 1¾in (5cm) "France" $140

B: This head is the same as a half-doll with mold number 22721 made by Sitzendorfer Porzellanfabrik and shown on PAGE 62 (top right photo). She has a yellow comb in her hair and fringe at her shoulder.

- 2½in (6cm) $140

Head with Long Base

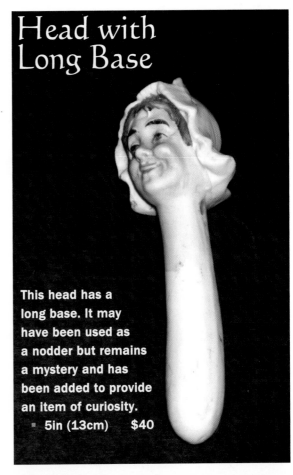

This head has a long base. It may have been used as a nodder but remains a mystery and has been added to provide an item of curiosity.

- 5in (13cm) $40

Lamps

Lamps were an important feature in milady's bedroom. Because everything French was considered an important decorating statement, the lamps in the bedroom were called boudoir lamps. The lamps were designed to sit on a dresser or be fastened to a bed, used as a means for spreading the aroma of perfume, or to rest on a bedside table. Some lamps were sold through stores or catalogs and some were sold as parts to assemble. The frames were used to make a shade that might match the décor of the room. Included here are full-figure porcelain lamps that were made by manufacturers of half-dolls. Sometimes the lamp's maker can be identified by the mold number or by the actual model of a half-doll that matches the upper portion of the figure on the lamp. The major manufacturers were Carl Schneider, F. & W. Goebel, I.W. Rice and Dressel, Kister & Co.

The height of the figurine is followed by the total height of the lamp. If the lamp has a mark or mold number it will be next, followed by the value.

Full-Figure Porcelain Lamps

MANY vintage lamps were modeled after the Victorian woman, Pierrots and Pierrettes, dancers, children and George and Martha Washington. If the manufacturer is known, a lamp will have greater value than a similar lamp that is unmarked.

A: This lamp of a Victorian woman dressed in a yellow gown with roses is unmarked and the manufacturer is unknown. She carries a fan in her left arm and her right hand lifts her dress so she can dance. The detail on the lamp is excellent, the painting is skillfully executed and the lamp is in excellent condition.

- 6in (15cm)   9in (23cm) $125

B: This model with a rare blue dress was molded after a painting of a dancer known as Mademoiselle Marie Anne de Cupis de Camargo. Frequently, this model was made with an orange dress. The molded bodice laces in the front while pink roses decorate the skirt. The dress is trimmed with white scallops. Both hands hold a scarf. The firm of Carl Schneider made the figurine. A small model of the figurine is found in the section on full-figures (see right-hand illustration on PAGE 111).

- 7in (18cm)   9¼in (24cm)   No. 14702 $165

C: This figurine of Pierrette wears an unusual headpiece that resembles a crown. Her red bodice has a skirt that flares out at the bottom and ends with two rows of multicolored ruffles. Under her skirt, she wears ruffled pantaloons of red, white and blue. A half moon decorates the upper portion of this unusual lamp by Carl Schneider. The facial features are delicate and the condition of the figurine is excellent.

- 6in (15cm)   8½in (22cm)   No. 16457 $215

Half-Dolls with Shades

SOME lamps were designed to hold a half-doll at the top, with the lower area covered with silk, creating the illusion of a skirt. The dolls were porcelain or ceramic.

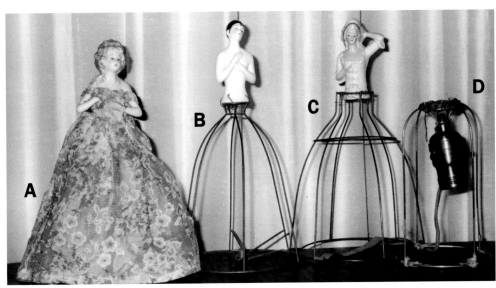

A: This figure shows the wire frame with the half-doll attached. The half-doll, a common model, is a clay ceramic that is less expensive than porcelain. Ceramic figurines lack eye appeal and are easily broken or chipped. This model is in excellent condition. Even though the skirt is soiled, she is valued as a sample of a finished vintage lamp.
- 3in (8cm) 10in (25cm) $70

B: This is a frame with a Pierrot. The half-doll was manufactured by Hertwig & Co. He is shown on PAGE 43 (top left illustration) without the frame. The frame would be wired and then covered with a skirt. The addition of a frame increases the value of a half-doll.
- 3½in (9cm) 11in (28cm) No. 4353 $115

C: This frame has another Hertwig & Co. half-doll. This is the model most frequently found on a frame. Even though she is perfect, she is inexpensive. This mold, without the frame, is found on PAGE 43 (bottom left illustration).
- 3¼in (9cm) 11¼in (29cm) No. 5023 $65

D: This frame has the electrical socket attached. It shows the parts of a lamp found under a skirt.
- 6in (15cm) No. 10 $10

The Lamps of Dressel, Kister & Co.

ANY item made by the company of Dressel, Kister & Co. is valued by the owner. Other manufacturers copied the work of this company but, generally, the copies lacked the artistry of the workmanship of Dressel, Kister & Co.

A: The half-doll on this lamp was manufactured by Dressel, Kister & Co. and was sculpted after a painting by Marie Louise Elisabeth Vigée-Lebrun of Madame Molé-Raymond. All that is left of the dress are some silk threads and a wire frame with ceramic fittings for a bulb. This half-doll is a rare model and, even though the skirt has melted, the lamp is still expensive.
- 14in (36cm) $550

B: This lamp is a medieval woman resembling the work of Dressel, Kister & Co. and is beautifully sculpted. It does not have a shade and it is unknown whether it was sold with a manufactured shade or the frame to be finished by milady. It is rare and considered a highly desirable item.
- 14in (36cm) 16½ in (42cm) $500

Perfume Lamps

PERFUME lamps have a tiny pocket at the back of the figurine. As the lamp warmed, the aroma of the perfume would be evident. Perfume lamps are desirable to collectors of figurines which were purchased for milady's boudoir.

A: This Victorian woman is wearing a long pink dress with a shawl wrapped around her. Both her apron and the comb which adorns her hair are decorated with gold trim. She appears to be a recent model.
   ▪ 7in (18cm)   unknown $115

B: The age of this figurine is unknown but it was manufactured by I.W. Rice. Sitting in a chair reading her book, she is a wonderful item and in excellent condition.
   ▪ 6in (15cm) $160

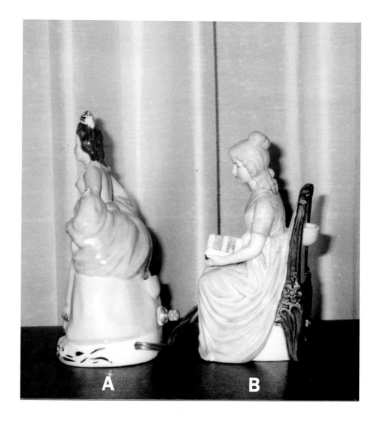

Lamps Made for Headboards

A boudoir lamp cost $1.15 in 1920. Some would hang from a headboard to provide a reading light. They were made with fabric over wire frames and a half-doll was used to add to the decoration. The value given is based upon the quality of the half-doll as well as the condition of the fabric.

The shape of this lamp is a half circle with a beautiful doll by Hertwig & Co. attached to the top. The "skirt" is open in the back where there is a fitting for the bulb. The fabric of the skirt is silk and the scarf is beautifully embroidered silk organdy. The doll holds castanets in her hands. Some of these boudoir lamps were sold in pairs, so each person in a double bed might have a light.
   ▪ 4½in (12cm)   8¼in (21cm)
      No. 6494 $350

TOP LEFT: This bed lamp has a half-doll made by Dressel, Kister & Co. The lamp is beautifully styled with a lady sitting on a quarter moon, her hands clasped under her chin. The lamp is soiled and the silk is melting but it is still a very desirable item, as the doll by itself would be expensive. The additional design of a lamp that beautifully complements the style of the half-doll is visually appealing.

- 10in (25cm)   10in (25cm) $525

MIDDLE LEFT: This is a set of three bed lamps. One would be hooked to the back of the bed and two would sit on the dressing table. The lamps that sit on the table are finished on the front and back. The one that hangs on the bed is finished on the front. All have the same model of half-doll and the quality of the half-doll is poor. The fabric is beginning to "melt" but the grouping is still beautiful.

STANDING:

- 13in x 10in (33cm x 25cm)

BED LAMP:

- 13in x 7in (33cm x 18cm)
  TOTAL VALUE OF SET: $395+

Fabric Lamps for Bed Stands

THE lamps shown on the right consist of a set of lamps and one other lamp. The backs of these lamps are unfinished while the front is in good condition. All the half-dolls used were made in Japan and are of poor quality. The fabric on the lamps remains soiled but intact.

A: This lamp is a half-doll sitting on a chair.

- 9¾in x 4¼in (25cm x 11cm)
  $125

B: This set of lamps has two half-dolls sitting but presented differently than the lamp previously described.

- 7½in x 4in (19cm x 10cm)
  PAIR: $250

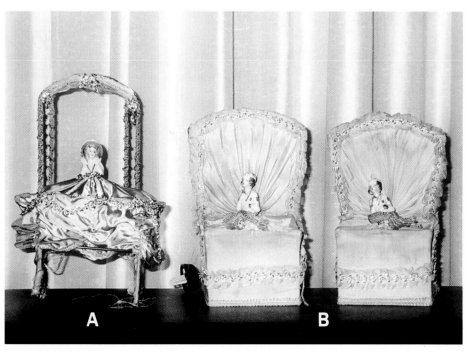

Perfume Bottles

The dressing table of the flapper held many articles including the perfume flask and bottle. The perfume flasks shown here are a full-figure of a person or animal. The flask is filled with perfume topped by a tiny cap. The cap can be metal or porcelain in a shape such as a crown. The cap/crown holds a small cork. A small amount of perfume would cling to the cork and be used by milady to pat the aroma where desired. The flasks are made of porcelain and are small, generally less than 4½in (12cm). Value is determined by the overall condition, the absence of chips, the condition of the cork, as well as the retention of paint on the flask. Other flasks held atomizers that would be pumped up and down until a spray of perfume was delivered, or rubberized bulbs that, when squeezed, produced a spray. The value is affected by the condition of the bulb.

Flasks

THE flasks featured on the right are china and are the smallest containers for perfume shown in this book.

A: This flask is that of a ram. This flask has a handle, a very unusual feature. The condition is excellent and the maker is Ernst Bohne Sohne.
- 3¾in x 1½in (8cm x 4cm) "[anchor mark]" $70

B: This flask is a mother monkey tending her young. Her appearance is sweet and comical and this would slightly increase the value. The condition of the flask is excellent and the maker is Ernst Bohne Sohne.
- 3½in x 1½in (9cm x 4cm) "[anchor mark]" $75

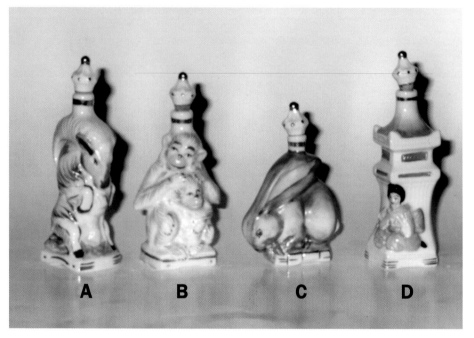

C: This bunny has a carrot in his paws. He has never been used. A hole in his cork suggests a dauber would have been inserted. He is from old stock discovered in an East German porcelain factory. The maker is Ernst Bohne Sohne.
- 3in x 2in (8cm x 5cm)   "[anchor mark]" $65

D: Oriental figures were very popular choices on flasks and this one features a Geisha. The stopper/cap is ceramic with a gilded tip. The flask has never been used and is in mint condition. The cork is intact. There are no chips and the paint is still intact. The bottom of the bottle carries the mark of the German manufacturer Ernst Bohne Sohne.
- 4in x 1½in (10cm x 4cm)   "[anchor mark]" $70

Small Individual Perfume Bottles

THE perfume bottles on the right were made of glass molded to look like women. They are painted on the exterior. Some have identification from their manufacturers while others do not.

A: The workmanship necessary for manufacturing this perfume bottle is greater than that for the perfume bottles **B** and **C**. This young woman holds her hands behind her head. The upper portion of the perfume bottle is similar to a half-doll without a base. She has a cork

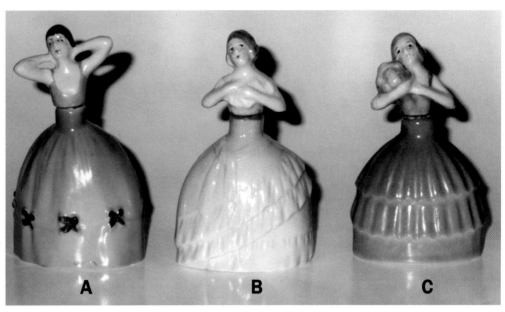

inserted inside this part of the bottle. A glass dauber is inserted into the cork to be used to put on perfume. The painting of her facial features is well done and her external condition is very good. The paint has not rubbed off and the glass is not chipped.

- 3½in (9cm)   No. 7627 $135

B: This perfume bottle is a woman wearing a gown with a white bodice and a pink skirt. The painting of her features lacks detail and her maker is unknown. The condition on the outside of the bottle is very good. The

cork with the dauber is missing and that decreases the value.

- 3in (8cm)   No. 7742 $85

C: This woman holds a pink bouquet next to her face. This mold is not as complicated as model **A**, as her arms remain close to her body. Her external condition is very good and her cork is intact with the dauber. The manufacturer is unknown.

- 3½in (9cm) $130

Perfume Sets

THE size of the perfume bottle is on the first line, the size of the powder jar is next, followed by the value of the total set.

This perfume set is black and was made in Japan. All the pieces have the same half-doll as the portion holding a stopper or cover. This set has one powder dish and two perfume bottles. All pieces are in excellent shape, however, the features are not well painted and lack clean detailing. The top of the set has half-dolls with scalloped skirts. The bottom portion is black. The inside of the jars is white. The manufacturer is unknown.

- 5in (13cm)
- 7½in (19cm) $300

This powder jar (A) is marked "ER-PHILA BAVARIA" and is photographed next to the jar made in Japan (B) for comparison. The powder jar is covered in a lustered purple paint. The sizes are identical; the quality is not. The features painted on the Bavarian jar top are superior to the Japanese model. The Bavarian model is enameled white on the inside and the Japanese is spray-painted. The value of a Bavarian set of perfume and powder holders is given here.

- 5in (13cm)   No. 3130/ 31
- 7½in (19cm)   No. 3130/--*
  $615

Numbers are illegible.

Other

THE two bottles on the left probably were made to hold cologne rather than perfume, as they are much larger than the other examples.

A: This perfume jar is an art deco model. The base of the jar is designed to hold lipstick tubes. The styling of this model is similar to those designed by Robj, a well-known French designer. The paint on the facial features shows wear. The Liane Company of France is the manufacturer.

- 9in x 6in (23cm x 15cm)   No. 237 $430

B: This jar is unusual. The top, designed to go with the bottom part, is not designed to finish the design of the bodice of the dress that is Victorian. The mold of the jar top is complicated, as the arms of the lady are away and then return to the body. The bottom of the jar fits the top and the colors are coordinated, but the period of fashion represented by each portion differs. The facial painting and the detail on the jar bottom are skillfully executed. She is in excellent condition but the manufacturer is unknown.

- 7½in (19cm) $235

Puff Dishes, Puffs and Patters

The figurines shown here are accurately called puff dishes, as that is what they were named in the original catalog. Collectors have called them trinket dishes, pin dishes and other names. They were intended to hold a bit of powder and the lady's puff. The puffs complemented the figure on the dish. In other words, a Pierrot (male clown) dish would hold a Pierrette (female clown) puff. It is unclear whether they were sold as a unit or separately. They were made in pairs, a male and female, of each type dish. Each model was made in several sizes. The primary porcelain manufacturer was Sitzendorfer Porzellanfabik which was eventually purchased by Gebrüder Voigt. The Sitzendorfer Porzellanfabrik is still in existence in East Germany. The company's mark of an "S" topped with a crown was used during the later period of production. (See Appendix A, page 131.)

Grouping some of these half-dolls allows for a comparison. After the description, the size is given, followed by the mark or mold number, if known, then the value and the identifying letter that should help you locate the item in the illustration.

Sitzendorfer Porzellanfabrik Models

THE two examples on the right are quite colorful and, while purchased separately, are a matched couple.

- **The pair as a couple: $290**

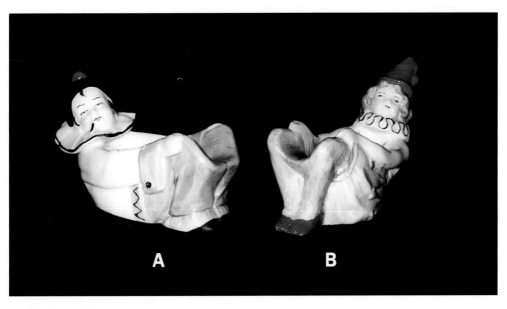

A: This model is a Pierrot. He wears a black skullcap, a ruffled collar and a clown suit of white, yellow and blue. A red ball tops his cap. Pierrot is smoking a cigarette and his head is turned to the right in such a manner that when placed next to Pierrette, he would to be looking at her. His features are well painted. The dish part is much narrower than other models, so it is possible he was made to be an ashtray.

- 4in (10cm)   No. 21629 $115

B: This Pierrette is slighter longer than the Pierrot to its left (**A**). Her head is turned to the left and her colors are identical to those of the Pierrot, except her stockings are lavender. She wears yellow bloomers and a clown hat that comes to a point. The facial painting is very good.

- 4¼in (11cm)   No. 26639 $115

THE pair seen on the right has swan's-down powder puffs that match their costumes.

■ **The Pierrette and Pierrot together, with the puffs: $900**

A: This Pierrette wears a costume of black, blue and white. Her middle section is rounded and her powder puff, with Pierrot as a handle, fits into the hollow and matches her costume. The sleeves on her costume are short. The facial painting is finely detailed and her face and arms are flesh-colored. Her head is tilted to the right and her shoulder-length hair is black. The value includes both pieces, without their matching puffs.

■ 5in (13cm)　　No. 24406　　$200

B: This Pierrot companion piece has a sad soulful expression with his face turned downward. He is painted in black and white, wears a black skullcap and

has three "spit" curls. He has long full sleeves. In his hollow he has a powder puff, which matches his costume, with the Pierrette as a handle. He is valued as a unit.

■ 4⅞in (12cm)　　No. 24106　　$200

LEFT: This pair is the same as the models **ABOVE**, but without the puffs. Pairs are rarely found so they are more valuable than two unmatched holders.

■ $500

Unknown German Manufacturer

This puff dish is large with a bowl that is 3in (8cm) wide. She is a flapper and is dressed in lounging pajamas. This size is difficult to find. Her features are well defined, but the paint has rubbed off in some areas and she is valued accordingly.

■ 7¼in (19cm)　　No. 8009　　$185

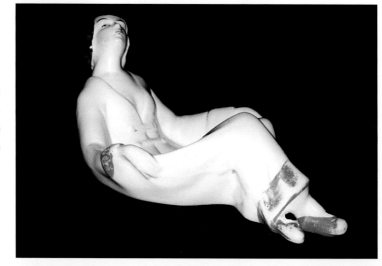

Japanese Puff Dish

This little Pierrot has well defined features. His face looks upward and his mouth is open and smiling. He wears clothing of gold luster paint with black accents and a white ruffled collar. He is marked "Made in Japan" on the underside.

- 4in (10cm) $85

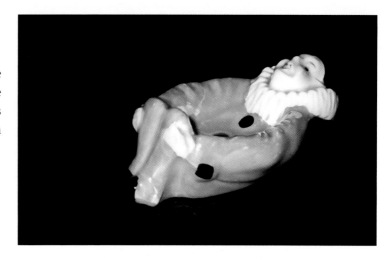

Patters

PATTERS were powder puffs on a stick. Generally the stick is around 11in (28cm) and covered with ribbon that complements the colors of the patter. Patters were made with bas-relief heads placed on the top of the puff and embellished with ribbon, or a head placed on the end of the stick with lace or ribbon covering the end of the head to make a collar.

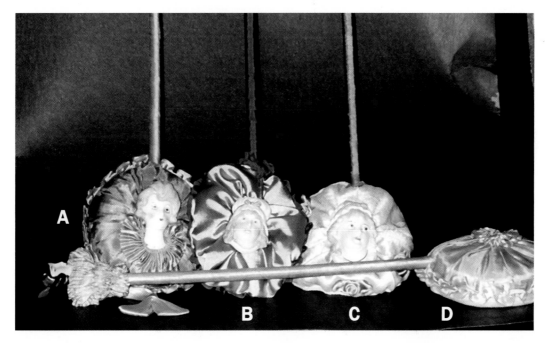

A: This blue patter is all-original. The manufacturer of the head, a bas-relief, was Carl Schneider.
- $185

B: This patter has a bas-relief made by A.W. Fr. Kister. The age is unknown.
- $120

C: This pink patter was made by A.W. Fr. Kister. The age is unknown.
- $120

D: This patter has the head on the handle. In the illustration, it is laying perpendicular to the other patters. It was manufactured around 1920 to 1930.
- $175

Various Other Items

There were many novel uses for half-dolls as seen throughout this book. The items in those previous sections represent objects that were manufactured in a large enough quantity that it was not difficult to find a representative sample. This value guide would be incomplete if the following items were not mentioned even though they are difficult to find. The values given reflect the quality of the item, the difficulty of the execution (molding and sculpting), the manufacturer, rarity of item and consumer interest.

Teapots

A few versions of these have been found, all of which are delightful. Reproductions are being made now, as well as new designs made by familiar porcelain manufacturers such as Limoges.

This teapot has a lady sitting atop so that she becomes the lid. The body of the teapot was molded to represent her full-length dress embellished with ruffles. It is marked "Ye Dainty Lady Teapot Reg. No. 824S71, Made in England."

- 5½in (14cm)   No. 824S71 $225

Pencil Toppers

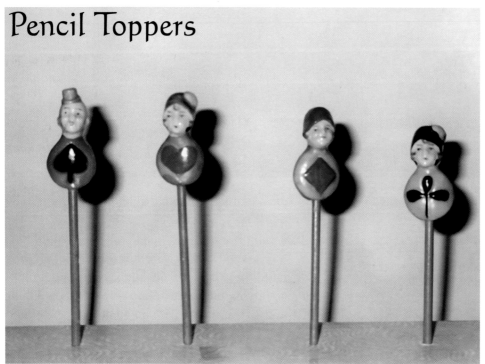

These four pencils were probably part of a set designed to be used when playing bridge, a game popular in the 1920s to the 1940s. The heads on the pencils are rather crudely painted and quite comical. They were placed where one would generally expect an eraser to be. Perhaps bridge players never made mistakes.

- 6in (15cm) $187

Hat Holders

HAT holders were designed to hold a hat while milady repaired her facial makeup or combed her hair. They were designed to hold the cloche, rather than the larger Gainsborough hats, and were popular during the end of the 1920s through the 1930s.

The hat holder was made from a dowel stick wrapped with silk ribbon that matched the color of the fabric covering the stand. The half-doll was seated next to the covered stand so that it appeared to be a cushion. At the top of the dowel was a padded half circle with a diameter of 2½in (6cm). The hat would be placed on the circle.

- 12in (31cm) $205

Pajama Cushions

HALF-DOLLS decorated the top of the cushions while the underside had an opening to allow pajamas to be hidden within. The values start at approximately $25.

Candy Containers

HALF-DOLLS have also been placed upon candy boxes. Old candy boxes are collected by themselves, as well as by half-doll collectors. To open the box, the whole top would be lifted in order to make the candy available. There are many variations, but all are relatively expensive. The value range of a candy container in very good condition would start at $225.

Umbrella Half-Dolls

BOTTOM LEFT: This half-doll holds her umbrella above her head. In her skirt, she might have velvet powder puffs stored ready to be used. Or she might have sachets wrapped in organdy and with fabric decoration.

- 11in (28cm) $185

Tea and Coffee Cozy

AT the turn of the century almost every table would have a cozy. They were responsible for keeping the liquid warm, as the pot was brought from the wood-burning stove to the table. The layers of fabric on the cozy would provide insulation. Cozies became decorative as ladies created handcrafted clothing for the half-doll. A coffee cozy's skirt was slightly longer than that of the tea cozy. Under the fabric of the skirt was a wire frame that would hold the material away from the pot. The wire frame was covered with fabric on the inside of the skirt so that none of the wire would be showing. The value of a cozy depends upon the condition of the fabric, the elaborateness of the costume and the value of the doll. Values generally start at $145

BOTTOM RIGHT: This model is in very good condition. The fabric is intact, the half-doll is not cracked or chipped and her arms are away from her body. Like most tea cozies, the half-doll looks too small for the body.

- 13in (33cm) $235

Flat Head Sewing Kits

SEWING kits had a bas-relief (flat) head that was placed upon a heavy paperboard. The entire ensemble looked much like a paper doll. The figure was covered with fabric that would be used as a cover to hide needles. Many of the bas-relief heads were made by the Carl Schneider Company. A recent sewing kit, as described, was 12½in (31cm) and sold for $125.

Faces and Legs

RIGHT: These heads were used as decorative items on muffs, as pins, on hats and whatever else could be imagined and were purchased in a range from $40 to $80.

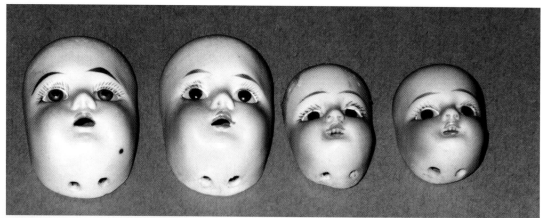

LEFT: These legs are assorted sizes and were placed on the side of a pincushion. They were left uncolored or were tinted pink prior to firing. Values range from $30 to $90, depending upon condition and size.

Squirter

This squirter was a naughty lady that could be filled with water at the top of the little opening on her head. If tipped slightly, liquid squirts from her breasts. It is a silly object and probably sat on a "gentleman's" bar top.

- 3½in (9cm) $105

Manufacturers' Marks, Logos and Trademarks

1. A.W. Fr. Kister	2. Dressel, Kister & Co.	3. Galluba & Hoffmann	4. F. & W. Goebel	5. Hertwig & Co.
6. Carl Schneider	7. Sitzendorfer Porzellanfabrik	8. Nippon (Made in Japan)	9. Bruno Schmidt	10. Conta & Boehme
11. Fulper Pottery Co.	12. Gebrüder Heubach	13. Herend.	14. Kämmer & Reinhardt	15. J.D. Kestner
16. Limbach	17. Shäfer & Vater	18. Volkstedt-Rudolstadt	19. Müller & Co.	20. G.H. Macheleid
21. Ernst Bohne Sohne	22. Artist Robj	23. Weiss, Kuhnert & Co.	24. Japanese	25. French

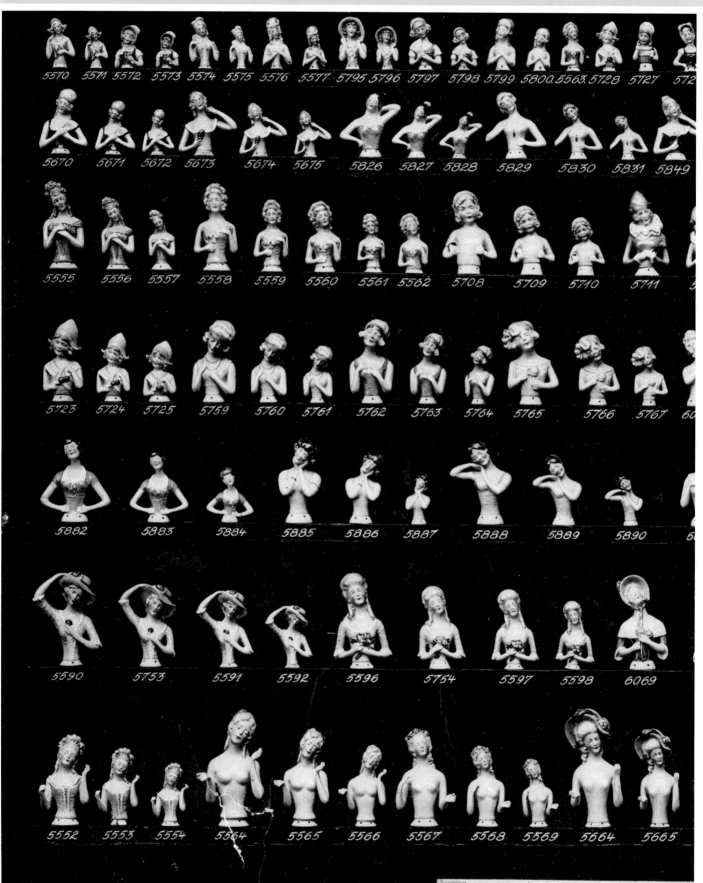

5726 6008 6009 6010 6011 6012 6013 5846 5847 5848 5667 5668 5669

849 5850 5851 6096 6097 6098 6099 6100 6101 6102 6103 6104

5712 5713 5714 5715 5716 5717 5718 5719 5720 5721 5722

6087 6087½ 6088 6089 6090 6090½ 6091 6092 6093 6093½ 6094 6095 6203

6078 6079 6080 6081 6082 6083 6084 6085 6086

6070 6071 6072 6073 6074 6075 6076 6077

5 5666 5593 5594 5595 5744 5599 5600 5601 5745

Sample Sets from the Hertwig & Co. Factory

TWO examples of boxed samples that Hertwig& Co. would send to wholesalers for the ordering of the half-dolls.

ILLUSTRATION of an antique mold for two sides of a half-doll, used in the manufacturing of a half-doll. The mold is probably from Weiss, Kühnert & Co.

ILLUSTRATION of the "Chocolate Lady" based on the portrait by Swiss artist Jean Etienne Liotard and used by Baker's Chocolate as its logo.

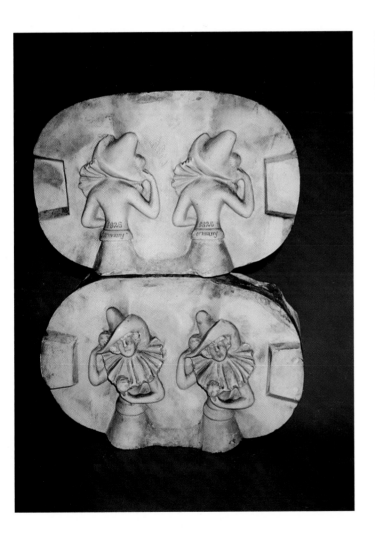

135

Resources

Internet Information

- www.worldcollectorsnet / magazine / issue12 / iss12p5.html
- www.arts.ilstu.edu / exhibits / perfare / deco.htm1
- www.costumes.org / pages / fashiondress / WW1 to WW2.htm
- http://alpha.furman.edu / ~kgossman / history / directory.htm
- http://www.costumes.org / pages / fashiondress / WW1toWW2.htm
- www.porcelainsite.com / hist_porc / hist_volk.shtm1
- www.porzellanseite.de / porcelain / marks /
- www.sitzendorf-porzellan.de/en/history
- http://users.skynet.be / rutrene / linkse01.htm1
- http://users.skynet.be / rutrene / marks33.htm1
- www.porcelainsite.com / porcelain / marks / volkstedt.shtm1
- http://www.meissen.us / history.html
- http://porcelainsite.com / thuringia / short_history.shtml
- www.hgtv.com / hgtv / ah /
- http://androsdance.tripod.com / biographies / elssler_fanny.htm
- http://libweb5.princeton.edu / visual_materials / delarue / Htmls / elssler.html
- http://www.dollsandlace.com / fanny.htm
- http://www.lkwdpl.org / wiohio / lind-jen.htm
- http://www.barum-museum.org / orig / htm1.htm
- http://www.sverigekontakt.o.se / jenny..htm

Auction Catalogs

- Cobb's Doll Auction. Columbus, OH: April 16, 1989.
- Cobb's Doll Auction. Columbus, OH: Feb. 4, 1990.
- Cobb's Doll Auction. Columbus, OH: June 24, 1990.
- Cobb's Doll Auction. Columbus, OH: Oct. 28, 1990.
- Cobb's Doll Auction. Johnstown, OH: May 18, 1997.
- Frasher's Doll Auctions. Inc. "Yesterday's Fancies." Oak Grove, MO: Nov. 15, 16 and 17, 1996.
- Richard W. Withington, Inc. "Dolls At Auction. Collection of Frieda Marion." Hillsboro, NH: May 29, 2003.
- Theriault. "Come, Said the Wind to the Leaves One Day." Annapolis, MD: Nov. 11, 2000.

Catalog Pages and Books from German Porcelain Factories

- Badedame Bathing Beauty Porzellan Art Deco Catalogue.
- Fox, Carl. *The Doll*. New York: Harry N. Abrams. Inc., Plate no. 120, 222-224.
- Hertwig & Co. Manufacturing page for wholesalers.
- Weiss. Kühnert & Co. Porzellanfabrik Catalogue.
- Weiss. Kühnert & Co. Porzellanfabrik Manufacturing page for wholesalers.

Bibliography

Angione, Genevieve. *All-Bisque and Half Bisque Dolls*. Exton, PA: Schiffer Publishing LTD., 1981.

Angione, Genevieve. "Pincushion Dolls." *Spinning Wheel*. December 1963.

Axe, John. *Collectible Dolls In National Costume*. Riverdale, MD: Hobby House Press Inc., 1977.

Cieslik, Jürgen and Marianne. *German Doll Encyclopedia 1800-1939*. Cumberland, MD: Hobby House Press. Inc., 1985.

Cieslik, Jürgen and Marianne. *German Doll Marks and Identification Book*. Cumberland, MD: Hobby House Press. Inc., 1986.

Cieslik, Jürgen and Marianne. *German Doll Studies*. Annapolis, MD: Gold Horse Publishing, 1999.

Coleman, Dorothy S., Elizabeth A. and Evelyn J. *The Collector's Book of Dolls' Clothes, Costumes in Miniature, 1700-1929*. New York: Crown Publishers. Inc., 1975.

Coleman, Dorothy S., Elizabeth A. and Evelyn J. *The Collector's Encyclopedia of Dolls*. New York: Crown Publishers Inc., 1968.

Coleman, Dorothy S., Elizabeth A. and Evelyn J. *The Collector's Encyclopedia of Dolls, Volume Two*. New York: Crown Publishers Inc., 1986.

Coleman, Dorothy, ed. *My Darling Dolls*. Princeton, NJ: The Pyne Press, 1972.

Eldridge, Charlotte. *The Godey Lady Doll*. New York: Hastings House Publishers, 1958.

Endo, Susan. *A Price Guide to Pincushion Dolls*. Covina, CA: Graphics United, 1980.

Endo, Susan. *Second Price Guide to Pincushion Dolls*. Covina, CA: Graphics United, 1990.

Foulke, Jan. *Insiders Guide to China Doll Collecting*. Grantsville, MD: Hobby House Press Inc., 1995.

Foulke, Jan. *Kestner, King of Dollmakers*. Cumberland, MD: Hobby House Press Inc., 1980.

Goodfellow, Caroline. *The Ultimate Doll Book*. New York: Dorling Kindersley, Inc., 1993.

Hedrick, Susan and Vilma Matchette. *World Colors Dolls and Dress*. Grantsville, MD: Hobby House Press, Inc., 1995.

Krombholz, Mary Gorham. *German Porcelain Dolls, 1836-2002*. Grantsville, MD: Hobby House Press, Inc., 2002.

Kybalova, Ludmila; Olga Herbenova; Milena Lamarova; with translation by Rosoux. *The Pictorial Encyclopedia of Fashion*. New York: Crown Publishers, Inc., 1966.

Lorrin, Marc and Shona. *The Half-Doll with Related Items, Makers and Values, Volume One*. Frostburg, MD: 1999.

Lorrin, Marc and Shona. *The Half-Doll with Related Items, Makers and Values, Volume Two*. Frostburg, MD: 2002.

Marion, Frieda and Norma Werner. *The Collector's Encyclopedia of Half-Dolls*. New York: Crown Publishers, Inc., 1979.

Marion, Frieda. "Quality Half-Dolls." *Silver Anniversary Convention Booklet UFDC Inc.* (1974): 42.

Marion, Frieda. "Those Lovely Half-Dolls." *International Doll and Miniature Convention Book UFDC. Inc.* (1975): 113-117.

Marion, Frieda. *China Half-Figures Called Pincushion Dolls*. Rowley, MA: Rowley Printing, Inc., 1974.

Marion, Frieda. *Value Update for The Collector's Encyclopedia of Half-Dolls*. New York: Crown Publishers, Inc., 1990.

Marion. Frieda and Norma Werner. *Dresser Dolls*. Paducah, KY: Collectors Books, 1883.

Merrill, Madeline Osborne. *The Art of Dolls, 1700-1940*. Cumberland, MD: Hobby House Press, Inc., 1985.

Revi, Albert Christian, ed. *Spinning Wheels Complete Book of Dolls*. New York: Galahad Books, 1975.

Richter, Lydia. *China, Parian & Bisque German Dolls*. Grantsville, MD: Hobby House Press, Inc., 1993.

Richter, Lydia. *Heubach Dolls*. Cumberland, MD: Hobby House Press, Inc., 1989.

Seeley, Mildred. *All-Bisque Dolls*. Oneonta, NY: Seeley's Ceramic Service. 1979.

Smith, Patricia. *Album of All Bisque Dolls. Identification and Value Guide*. Paducah, KY: Collector Books. 1992.

St. George, Eleanor. *Old Dolls*. New York: M. Barrows and Co., Inc., 1950.

St. George, Eleanor. *The Dolls of Yesterday*. New York: Charles Scribner's Sons, 1948.

Theriault, Florence, ed. *The Ladies of Hertwig*. Annapolis, MD: Gold Horse Publishing, 2003.

Theriault, Florence. *Hertwig and Co. Archives, 1890-1937*. Annapolis, MD: Gold Horse Publishing, 2000.

Unger, Jorg. "Weiss, Kuhnert and Co., Visiting a Thuringian Porcelain Factory." *Doll News*. Winter 2001: 40-43.

Van Patten, Joan F. and Linda Lau. *Nippon Dolls and Playthings*. Paducah, KY: Collector Books, 2001.

Vogel, Janice and Richard, Editor. *Contra & Boehme* (a copy of the catalog issued around 1912 to 1917). Ocala, FL: 2001

Vogel, Janice and Richard. *Contra & Boehme Porcelain, Identification and Value Guide*. Ocala, FL: 2001

Vogel, Janice and Richard. *Victorian Trinket Boxes, A Handbook with Price Guide for the Collector*. Ocala, FL: Poßneck Publishing Company, 1996.

Von Ulrich Klever, Hearausgegeben. *Nippes*. Munchen, Germany: Wilhelm Heyne Verlag, 1980.

Mold Numbers

Mold #	Manufacturer	Page #
0 – 999		
4 1/2	F. & W. Goebel	93
4 9954	F. & W. Goebel	93
5 1/2	F. & W. Goebel	93
7	Unknown	116
8/1	F. & W. Goebel	94
10	Unknown	119
10/2	Unknown	117
25 4 1/2	F. & W. Goebel	94
36	Unknown	116
40	Unknown	100
51B8 10a	Kestner & Co.	73
95	Unknown	115
97v	Kestner & Co.	73
99/54	F. & W. Goebel	28
109	F. & W. Goebel	30
121.3	F. & W. Goebel	31
180 0/0	F. & W. Goebel	32
181 3 1/2	F. & W. Goebel	93
181 4 1/2	F. & W. Goebel	93
237	Liane Company	124
290	Herend	72
311	Herend	72
320	F. & W. Goebel	32
351	Liane Company	97
373	F. & W. Goebel	34
406/6	F. & W. Goebel	32
416	Unknown	80
421.3 1/2	F. & W. Goebel	31
455	F. & W. Goebel	31
678	Unknown	107
824S71	Unknown	128
1000 – 1999		
1005	Unknown	108
1105/5	F. & W. Goebel	29
1308.3	F. & W. Goebel	32
1726	Unknown	87
1806	F. & W. Goebel	32
1936	Weiss, Kühnert & Co.	67
2000 – 2999		
2348	Hertwig & Co.	41
2420	Hertwig & Co.	36
2623	Hertwig & Co.	43
2978	Hertwig & Co.	35
3000 – 3999		
3100	Unknown	78
3130/31	Erphila Bavaria	124
3150	Unknown	99
3401	F. & W. Goebel	31
3497	Unknown	97
3538a	Baehr & Proeschild	70
3575	Unknown	99
3613	Hertwig & Co.	36
3635	Unknown	115
3659	Unknown	24
3684 (arms)	Baehr & Proeschild	70
3806	Galluba & Hofmann	24
3867	Galluba & Hofmann	92
3986	Dressel, Kister & Co.	16
3992	Dressel, Kister & Co.	16
3993	Dressel, Kister & Co.	16
4000 – 4999		
4133	Dressel, Kister & Co.	17
4136	Dressel, Kister & Co.	17
4183	Hertwig & Co.	41
4274	Dressel, Kister & Co.	15
4275	Dressel, Kister & Co.	15
4339	Hertwig & Co.	37
4344	Hertwig & Co.	43
4345	Hertwig & Co.	41
4346	Hertwig & Co.	44
4347	Hertwig & Co.	39
4348	Hertwig & Co.	43
4349	Hertwig & Co.	42
4350	Hertwig & Co.	43
4351	Hertwig & Co.	41
4352	Hertwig & Co.	44
4353	Hertwig & Co.	43,119
4354	Hertwig & Co.	41,42
4355	Hertwig & Co.	39
4356	Hertwig & Co.	43
4409	Unknown	95
4433	Unknown	83
4469	Dressel, Kister & Co.	12
4567	Dressel, Kister & Co.	12
4658	Dressel, Kister & Co.	12
4659	Dressel, Kister & Co.	12
4837	Unknown	117
4885	Hertwig & Co.	103
4916	Dressel, Kister & Co.	17
4920	Dressel, Kister & Co.	15
4927	Galluba & Hofmann	27
5000 – 5999		
5023	Hertwig & Co.	43,119
5063	Hertwig & Co.	39
5096	Unknown	113
5125	Hertwig & Co.	41
5160	Hertwig & Co.	41
5167	Weiss, Kühnert & Co.	68
5168	Weiss, Kühnert & Co.	68
5175	Hertwig & Co.	39
52B11a	Kestner & Co.	73

Mold #	Manufacturer	Page #
5249	Unknown	81
5255	Foulds & Freure	22
5273 (base)	Sitzendorfer Porzellanfabrik	112
5280	Hertwig & Co.	37
5289	Hertwig & Co.	37
5333	Hertwig & Co.	42
5360 (base)	Sitzendorfer Porzellanfabrik	112
5382	Hertwig & Co.	36
5400	Foulds & Freure	22
5403	Unknown	106
5475	Unknown	112
5485	Foulds & Freure	22
5493	Hertwig & Co.	39
5496	Foulds & Freure	22
5501	Hertwig & Co.	44
5501	Weiss, Kühnert & Co.	64
5509	Hertwig & Co.	43
5509	Hertwig & Co.	44
5541 (base)	Carl Schneider	114
5543	Hertwig & Co.	41
5553	Weiss, Kühnert & Co.	63
5554	Weiss, Kühnert & Co.	63
5555	Weiss, Kühnert & Co.	63
5556	Weiss, Kühnert & Co.	63
5558	Weiss, Kühnert & Co.	68
5559	Hertwig & Co.	44
5559	Weiss, Kühnert & Co.	64
5561	Weiss, Kühnert & Co.	64,68
5561	Weiss, Kühnert & Co.	68
5562	Weiss, Kühnert & Co.	68
5580	Hertwig & Co.	43
5581	Hertwig & Co.	42
5582	Hertwig & Co.	41
5590	Weiss, Kühnert & Co.	66
5591	Weiss, Kühnert & Co.	66
5592	Weiss, Kühnert & Co.	66
5593	Weiss, Kühnert & Co.	66
5594	Weiss, Kühnert & Co.	66
5595	Weiss, Kühnert & Co.	66
5596	Weiss, Kühnert & Co.	64
5624	Hertwig & Co.	42
5626	Hertwig & Co.	41
5642	Galluba & Hofmann	25
5645	Galluba & Hofmann	24
5664	Weiss, Kühnert & Co.	63
5645f	Galluba & Hofmann	24
5665	Weiss, Kühnert & Co.	63
5666	Weiss, Kühnert & Co.	63
5667	Weiss, Kühnert & Co.	66
5668	Weiss, Kühnert & Co.	66
5669	Weiss, Kühnert & Co.	66
5692	Galluba & Hofmann	24
5706	Galluba & Hofmann	25
5711	Weiss, Kühnert & Co.	66
5712	Weiss, Kühnert & Co.	66
5713	Weiss, Kühnert & Co.	66
5715	Weiss, Kühnert & Co.	65
5716	Weiss, Kühnert & Co.	65

Mold #	Manufacturer	Page #
5717	Weiss, Kühnert & Co.	65
5719	Weiss, Kühnert & Co.	64
5722	Unknown	109
5723	Carl Schneider	108
5723	Weiss, Kühnert & Co.	68
5724	Carl Schneider	108
5724	Weiss, Kühnert & Co.	68
5725	Weiss, Kühnert & Co.	68
5753	Weiss, Kühnert & Co.	66
5793	Weiss, Kühnert & Co.	67
5794	Weiss, Kühnert & Co.	67
5795	Weiss, Kühnert & Co.	67
5796	Weiss, Kühnert & Co.	67
5797	Weiss, Kühnert & Co.	68
5798	Weiss, Kühnert & Co.	68
5826	Hertwig & Co.	39
5856	Unknown	114
5857	Weiss, Kühnert & Co.	67
5858	Weiss, Kühnert & Co.	67
5884	Hertwig & Co.	36
5885	Weiss, Kühnert & Co.	66
5886	Weiss, Kühnert & Co.	66
5887	Weiss, Kühnert & Co.	66
5888	Weiss, Kühnert & Co.	66
5889	Weiss, Kühnert & Co.	66
5890	Weiss, Kühnert & Co.	66
5953	Unknown	78
6000 – 6999		
6002	Unknown	101
6031	Hertwig & Co.	36
6037	Hertwig & Co.	41
6069	Weiss, Kühnert & Co.	65
6070	Weiss, Kühnert & Co.	65
6071	Weiss, Kühnert & Co.	65
6072	Weiss, Kühnert & Co.	67
6072 (base)	Unknown	113
6073	Weiss, Kühnert & Co.	67
6074	Weiss, Kühnert & Co.	67
6078	Hertwig & Co.	36
6086	Weiss, Kühnert & Co.	67
6088	Weiss, Kühnert & Co.	67
6089	Weiss, Kühnert & Co.	67
6102	Weiss, Kühnert & Co.	65,114
6103	Weiss, Kühnert & Co.	65
6237	Hertwig & Co.	40
6237	Unknown	82
6293	Weiss, Kühnert & Co.	67
6327	Unknown	116
6331	Unknown	115
6342	Hertwig & Co.	43
6344	Unknown	110
6347	Hertwig & Co.	43
6348	Unknown	110
6348	Weiss, Kühnert & Co.	64
6386	Hertwig & Co.	35,108
6443	Hertwig & Co.	35,108
6449	Hertwig & Co.	35
6494	Hertwig & Co.	108,120

Mold #	Manufacturer	Page #
6512	Hertwig & Co.	43
6715	Unknown	79
6903	Unknown	86
6987 1/2	Weiss, Kühnert & Co.	67
7000 – 7999		
7042	Hertwig & Co.	38
7043	Hertwig & Co.	38
7046	Hertwig & Co.	40
7131	Unknown	79
7389	Unknown	82
7396	Hertwig & Co.	38
7398	Hertwig & Co.	38
7403	Unknown	109
7476 (base)	Unknown	113
7627	Unknown	123
7645	Hertwig & Co.	38
7646	Hertwig & Co.	38
7647	Hertwig & Co.	38
7648	Hertwig & Co.	38
7662	Hertwig & Co.	38
7663	Hertwig & Co.	38
7664	Hertwig & Co.	38
7665	Hertwig & Co.	38
7740	Hertwig & Co.	38
7741	Hertwig & Co.	38
7742	Unknown	13
7742	Unknown	123
7743	Hertwig & Co.	38
7744	Hertwig & Co.	38
7747	Hertwig & Co.	38
7946	Hertwig & Co.	40
8000 – 8999		
8009	Unknown	126
8026	Hertwig & Co.	40
8030	Hertwig & Co.	43
8032	Hertwig & Co.	44
8033	Hertwig & Co.	39
8034	Hertwig & Co.	43
8036	Hertwig & Co.	37
8037	Hertwig & Co.	39
8039	Hertwig & Co.	87
8050	Hertwig & Co.	41,86
8200 (base)	Sitzendorfer Porzellanfabrik	112
8212	Hertwig & Co.	38
8479	Galluba & Hofmann	25
8576	Unknown	89
8577	Unknown	89
8709	Hertwig & Co.	86
8769	Unknown	108
8779	Unknown	108
8874	Hertwig & Co.	39
9000 – 9999		
9001	Foulds & Freure	20
9002	Foulds & Freure	20
9003	Foulds & Freure	20
9088	Unknown	89
9092	Unknown	85
9093	Unknown	85

Mold #	Manufacturer	Page #
9190	Galluba & Hofmann	91
9191	Galluba & Hofmann	91
9200	Ernst Bohne Sohne	69
9250	Galluba & Hofmann	25
9397	Galluba & Hofmann	92
9398	Galluba & Hofmann	92
9435	Müller and Co.	113
9615	Foulds & Freure	22
9618	Foulds & Freure	20
9619	Foulds & Freure	20
9624	Foulds & Freure	21
9806	Galluba & Hofmann	23
9828	Galluba & Hofmann	23
9954	F. & W. Goebel	28
10000 – 10999		
10016	Carl Schneider	55
10041	Carl Schneider	51
10250 (base)	Unknown	113
10424/2	Gebrüder Heubach	71
10424/3	Gerbrüder Heubach	71
10424/4	Gebrüder Heubach	71
11000 – 11999		
11133	Carl Schneider	51
11937	Carl Schneider	52
12000 – 12999		
12286	Carl Schneider	52
12287	Carl Schneider	54
12527	Carl Schneider	55,108
12529	Carl Schneider	108
12736	Carl Schneider	54
12756	Carl Schneider	51
12762	Carl Schneider	51
12763	Carl Schneider	51
13000 – 13999		
13016	Carl Schneider	56
13268	Carl Schneider	51
13420	Carl Schneider	54
13475	Carl Schneider	48
13704	Carl Schneider	57
13752	Carl Schneider	56
13853	Carl Schneider	94
13910	Carl Schneider	49
13911	Carl Schneider	54
13911	Carl Schneider	51,54
13945	Carl Schneider	51
13952	Carl Schneider	51
14000 – 14999		
14165	Unknown	82
14178	Carl Schneider	55
14260	Carl Schneider	114
14264	Carl Schneider	49
14266	Carl Schneider	49
14267	Carl Schneider	49
14274	Carl Schneider	50
14275	Carl Schneider	50
14277	Carl Schneider	50
14281	Carl Schneider	51
14284	Carl Schneider	51

Mold #	Manufacturer	Page #
14291	Carl Schneider	105
14341	Carl Schneider	106
14377	Carl Schneider	49
14389	Carl Schneider	50,51
14391	Carl Schneider	51
14392	Carl Schneider	106
14393	Carl Schneider	106
14416	Carl Schneider	55
14503	Carl Schneider	58
14504	Carl Schneider	54
14505	Carl Schneider	54
14506	Carl Schneider	53
14508	Carl Schneider	56
14605	Carl Schneider	49
14686	Carl Schneider	57
14702	Carl Schneider	118
14753	Carl Schneider	51
14754	Carl Schneider	50
14756	Carl Schneider	51
14802	Carl Schneider	58
14843	Carl Schneider	111
14968	Carl Schneider	52
14979	Carl Schneider	50
14980	Carl Schneider	50
14991	Carl Schneider	49
15000 – 15999		
15140	Unknown	111
15142	Carl Schneider	52
15272	Carl Schneider	50
15273	Carl Schneider	50
15278	Carl Schneider	50
15308 (base)	Carl Schneider	112
15508	Carl Schneider	57
16000 – 16999		
16218	Unknown	110
16457	Carl Schneider	118
16952	Carl Schneider	55
17000 – 17999		
17039	Carl Schneider	48
17243	Carl Schneider	52
17558	Unknown	79
18000 – 18999		
18001	Carl Schneider	53
19000 – 19999		
19098	Carl Schneider	53
19421	Unknown	106
19427	Unknown	106
21000 – 21999		
21275	Sitzendorfer Porzellanfabrik	61
21276	Sitzendorfer Porzellanfabrik	61
21629	Sitzendorfer Porzellanfabrik	125
21634	Sitzendorfer Porzellanfabrik	61
22000 – 22999		
22179	Sitzendorfer Porzellanfabrik	59
22205	Sitzendorfer Porzellanfabrik	61
22206	Sitzendorfer Porzellanfabrik	61
22237	Unknown	77

Mold #	Manufacturer	Page #
22473	Sitzendorfer Porzellanfabrik	59
22479	Sitzendorfer Porzellanfabrik	59
22549	Sitzendorfer Porzellanfabrik	61
22614	Sitzendorfer Porzellanfabrik	61
22670	Sitzendorfer Porzellanfabrik	60
22674	Sitzendorfer Porzellanfabrik	60
22687	Sitzendorfer Porzellanfabrik	62,112
22721	Sitzendorfer Porzellanfabrik	62
22854	Sitzendorfer Porzellanfabrik	60
22871	Sitzendorfer Porzellanfabrik	60
23000 – 23999		
23007	Sitzendorfer Porzellanfabrik	60
23008	Sitzendorfer Porzellanfabrik	60
23146	Sitzendorfer Porzellanfabrik	60
23151	Unknown	105
23435	Sitzendorfer Porzellanfabrik	61
23451	Unknown	105
24000 – 24999		
24106	Unknown	126
24406	Unknown	126
24699	Sitzendorfer Porzellanfabrik	60
25000 – 80000		
25027	Sitzendorfer Porzellanfabrik	105
26022 (base)	Sitzendorfer Porzellanfabrik	114
26639	Sitzendorfer Porzellanfabrik	125
27442	Sitzendorfer Porzellanfabrik	62
76792	Unknown	104

LETTERED BEGINNING		
BT 1/0	F. & W. Goebel	30
BT 154	F. & W. Goebel	33
BT 181	F. & W. Goebel	93
BT410/4/4	F. & W. Goebel	31
BT455/2/0	F. & W. Goebel	31
D326	A.W. Fr. Kister	94
ex 222	F. & W. Goebel	34
R.T. 300 5 1/2	F. & W. Goebel	32
Sp1120	Unknown	82
WG 9301	F. & W. Goebel	33
WG3	F. & W. Goebel	28,29
WG4	F. & W. Goebel	29,30,31
WG5	F. & W. Goebel	30

ILLEGIBLE OR MISSING		
No. -011*	Unknown	117
No. ---08*	Carl Schneider	48
No. -525*	Unknown	78
No. --60*	Unknown	117
No. ---75*	Carl Schneider	87
No. ---91	Unknown	116
3130/--*	Unknown	124
3623*	Hertwig & Co.	43
555-*	Foulds & Freure	22
765-*	Unknown	82
WG-*	F. & W. Goebel	30

= numbers missing or illegible

Index

About the Author

SALLY VAN LUVEN'S interest in dolls was sparked by the story told about her maternal grandmother, Hettie Peters, who belonged to the religious sect called the Dunkards (Church of the Brethren). As a young girl, Hettie won a doll as a prize for reciting a poem. When she arrived home, however, her father took the doll from her, tied it to a clothesline and burned it, as he believed it was evil and broke the first commandment because it had a face. Probably because of this incident, Sally received books rather than dolls when she was growing up, even though she longed for a doll.

After her children were grown, Sally had the time to renew her interest in dolls and began to buy antique dolls. For over sixteen years, Sally has bought and sold dolls and counts the half-dolls as her favorites. Upon discovering there was no definitive value guide for these collectibles, she decided to remedy the situation by researching and compiling the information for publication.

The author, who holds a Ph.D. in Family Studies, is a member of NADDA (National Antique Doll Dealers Association) and UFDC (United Federation of Doll Clubs, Inc.).